THE SURVIVAL GREENHOUSE

An Eco-system  Approach to
Home Food Production
by James DeKorne

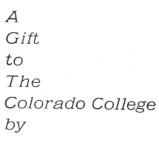

THE SURVIVAL GREENHOUSE

An Eco-system Approach to Home Food Production

James B. DeKorne

Illustrations by
Elizabeth and James DeKorne

Peace Press
1978

ACKNOWLEDGEMENTS

First, my love and gratitute to Carolyn Allers, without whose
help this book would not exist.
To Peter van Dresser, my philosophical mentor and the man who
many years ago started me on this path.
To David House, Michael Hackleman, Barbara Conrad, and
William Zelezny, who loved us when we were down and out.
To Michael Saxton, who opened my mind to the importance of
carbon dioxide, and to John Todd, Bill McLarney and Daniel
Metnick, for their insights and help with aquaculture.
To Ken Orvis, whose willing hands and strong back gave us a
greenhouse long before I could have built it alone.
And last, but certainly not least, to my loving wife Elizabeth, who
typeset this book and did all of the layout.

Second Edition
Peace Press, 1978

Peace Press, Inc.
3828 Willat Avenue
Culver City, California 90230
Originally published by The Walden Foundation in 1975

Printed in the United States of America
by Peace Press, Inc.

Library of Congress Catalog Number 78-52888
International Standard Book Number 0-915238-20-9

9 8 7 6 5 4 3 2 1

This book is dedicated to everyone
who has ever been on food stamps.

CONTENTS

PHOTOS

FIGURES

INTRODUCTORY CONCEPTS

I

"Ecology" is one of those well-worn words
which has had its original meaning expanded to
include connotations ranging from pollution and
population control to conservation. Automobile
bumper stickers shout the phrase: "Ecology
Now!" and oil companies pay large sums of
money for advertisements designed to convince
us of their "concern for ecology." A word
coined less than a century ago, and less than
twenty years ago familiar only to biologists and
science teachers, has today become a part of
everyone's vocabulary. It is a matter of some
speculation, however, as to how many of us
really understand the word and its implications.

The dictionary tells us that ecology is "the
scientific study of plants and animals in relation
to their natural environment." In this classical
definition of the word, we see that ecology is,
above all, a way of perceiving reality. One can
learn a great deal about a frog by dissecting it,
naming its parts, and observing how they all fit
together to make a living organism, but the
knowledge so gained is probably the least important information to be gained about the frog.

To really understand the nature of this creature one must study it in relation to the eco-system of which it is a part - how is the frog adapted to its environment? What role does it play in that environment's balance of forces? When one learns to view reality in this relational sense, it soon becomes apparent that central to the ecological frame of reference is the perception that everything is related to everything else. The laws of ecology are nothing less than the matrix underlying the phenomenon we call nature.

Ecology is a scientific discipline, subject to the same rules of discourse and proof that regulate any science. Yet, implicit in the ecological viewpoint is a wholeness which is more compatible with Eastern and American Indian world views than with the Platonic dualism which, in the guise of Western scientific and philosophical thought, sees man apart from nature rather than a part of nature. This is important, because it was in the West that the Industrial Revolution began, and it was in the Industrial Revolution that the ecological imbalances we are now trying to cope with had their beginning. The mind which is concerned with parts rather than wholes is the mind that dissects the frog to see how it works, and ignores the eco-system of which the frog is an integral part. Such a mind invents a machine without examining how the machine will affect the environment it modifies. A mind that sees a frog as a whole system will see an internal combustion engine as a whole system, and in this admittedly engrossing preoccupation fail to realize that there is only one system, and that is nature itself.

If one studies a graph showing world population growth from the sixth millenium B. C. projected to the year 2000, one quickly notes that the increase in human population was negligible until, in the middle of the 18th century, the Industrial Revolution began. The direct link between population growth and the rise of technology is extremely significant, for it is these two factors: overpopulation and pollution of the environment by technology and its waste products, which has brought the world to the brink of catastrophe. Before the Industrial Revolution, human population was relatively stable - natural forces in the environment kept everything in balance. The rapid rise in technology, however, caused two things which upset this natural balance: first, in the improvement of living standards brought about by, among other things, medicines and sophisticated agricultural techniques, the population increased rapidly, and second, the new technology introduced waste products into the world eco-system which were incapable of being assimilated or recycled by natural processes. It has become a truism to state that overpopulation is the key problem in world ecology. This is not strictly accurate - it is technology which must be blamed if one wants to find the real lowest common denominator. Without the rise in technology there could never have been a rise in population.

It is an irrefutable law of nature that organisms which cannot adapt to their environment are doomed to extinction. Man has so altered his environment, and so adapted himself to these alterations, that should any sudden change take place in the world eco-system it is doubtful that many individuals could survive. Technology has estranged us from nature - we relate to machine processes rather than natural ones. Buckminster Fuller has pointed out our frightening dependence on technology by observing: "Take away the power lines and the machinery from America, Russia, and all the world's industrialized countries - and within six months more than two billion people will, swiftly and painfully, starve to death."

The technological innovations which have been hailed as the greatest achievements of civilization are the very factors which threaten to destroy it. It is ironic to note that the "underdeveloped" countries with whom the industrialized west is so concerned about sharing its technologically sophisticated agricultural techniques, is the only segment of the world population likely to survive the coming crunch - precisely because it is not dependent upon high technology! Despite all of his present problems, the third-world farmer who still knows how to plow with oxen and fertilize with manure will be better adapted than the agribusinessman to feed himself when petroleum and petroleum-based chemical fertilizers are no longer available.

Historically in the West, science, capitalism and war have been the midwives of high technology. Science discovers the natural principles and thinks up their applications, capital investment produces the devices that manifest the principles, and war, fought to gain or maintain markets, refines many of the devices and brings about the need for further scientific research. Many, if not most of the technological miracles of the past thirty years are the spin-

4

off from research required by the needs of the military. Such an interlocking dependency can only lead to the kind of world we have now - a world of atomic weapons and ICBMs. Who, upon sober reflection, would want the benefits of an all-transistor TV set at such a price?

Factories are machines which transform raw materials (natural resources) into finished products. Under a capitalistic economic system, these "factory-machines" must continue to work in order to pay off their investment costs and produce a profit for their owner-investors. Since the law of supply and demand acts as a natural check to the profit motive, the capitalist system requires the artificial maintenance of a continuous demand for the products of the factory-machine. Such a system requires the creation of want, of need, even if no need ever existed before. Thus, an automobile, which could be made to last thirty years, is made to last less than ten years and, on top of that, is changed stylistically every year to further facilitate early obsolescence. While this may fill the coffers of the corporations, it strips the earth of its non-renewable resources, and throws natural systems into chaotic imbalance.

Put bluntly, "profit" means getting more out of something than you put into it - such is the rationale of the cancer cell. Ghandi was criticizing the capitalist system as much as stating a basic ecological principle when he said: "Nature provides enough for every man's need, but not enough for every man's greed."

Profit is what a man makes when he plants

a field of potatoes, harvests the crop, and then sells it for more money than the value of his investment and labor. The man who buys the potatoes must in turn charge more for his investment and labor to recoup the first man's "profit" and, incidently, to gain a profit for himself. In a society, this process is repeated over and over again, until it ultimately results in a debasement of standards of value, or, put in economic terms: inflation. The inflation-depression, boom and bust economic cycle is an integral part of a capitalistic system.

Ecology tells us that all forces in nature exist in balance with each other; capitalism tells us that there is such a thing as a free lunch, that you can get more out of something than you put into it. Emphasis on profit, and ignorance of natural checks and balances fosters the illusion of "progress," which, in the present economic sense means growth as synonymous with improvement. This is America's most dangerous semantic hallucination - Growth and Improvement are in no way synonyms, as anyone who lives in the ghetto of any modern American city will tell you.

A man who uses machines to interact with a steel and concrete world, loses touch with the great lessons to be learned from ecological systems. Farmers who relate to their land in terms of tractors, combines, chemical fertilizers and the economic manipulations of the Chicago grain market are equally out of touch with ecological reality. The short-term gains brought about by their profit-oriented perceptions only further blind them to the inevitable long term ecological consequences of such perception.

The profit motive is "selfish" in that it strives to gain something at the expense of something, or someone, else. Someone must lose for me to gain. Now, self-preservation is a natural force in everyone's life, and there is nothing "wrong" with it, since it insures survival of both individual and species. However, in human culture when selfish motivations exceed the basic requirements of the individual to survive in reasonable comfort, and, moreover, are fulfilled at the expense of the environment and the individual's fellow creatures, then both individual and society suffer, since in the long run an individual's welfare is dependent upon the welfare of the society in which he lives. Such selfish motivations are contrary to the basic teachings of all the world's major religions, as well as contrary to ecological laws. Animals in ecological harmony do not take more from nature than they give back. If each lion sought a "profit" of more zebras than it could eat, there soon would be none left and all lions would starve. Man is the only animal that deliberately takes more from his environment than he needs for his own survival and basic well-being.

A profit-oriented economic system can only thrive in an environment of abundant natural resources and energy. Like the cancer cells which eventually destroy their host and themselves as well, a capitalist economic system, if continued, must eventually destroy itself as it consumes resources beyond the point of recovery. Current world political and economic conditions reflect this situation, and it is no solace to note that the only economic frame of reference which stands ready to replace capitalism is communism.

Communism, invented to counter the in-
humane excesses of the 19th century capitalist
"robber barons," is no improvement, since it
only replaces one form of tyranny with another
in its cynical (though cold-bloodedly pragmatic)
assumption that moral individualism is impossible. Capitalism insists on the individual's
"right" to be a predator. Communism, in
curbing this "right," insists that the individual
cease being an individual entirely. (The choice
between being eaten alive by a lion or by a
million fire ants is not much of a choice.) In
addition, communism is essentially "people's
capitalism" - and, as an economic system, it
is not inherently more "ecological" or less
damaging to natural systems than capitalism is,
though because of its totalitarian nature it could
conceivably enforce ecologically sound practices.
Neither system is adequate to cope with the real
problems we face.

What the world needs desperately is a phi-
losophy of natural economics. Both the word
ecology and economy have the same root and,
if one meditates long enough on the meaning of
each, it becomes obvious that they are in a very
real sense synonyms. What the world has now
is an economy of consumption, not an economy
of conservation, and in capitalism and communism we have two economic dinosaurs struggling
for control of a technological tar pit. History
may yet prove that high technology has negative
survival value for any civilization which em-
braces it.

On the other hand, it cannot be denied that
technology has brought about tremendous im-

provements in our standard of living - very few
of us would voluntarily return to the living conditions of the 19th, let alone the 17th, century.
Surely an informed populace should be able to
develop a technologically sophisticated way of
life consistent with ecological reality.

Central to any such endeavor would be the
exclusive use of non-polluting, renewable
energy sources - energy from the sun, wind,
tides, composted wastes, etc. Anyone who has
examined and worked with it, however, will
immediately tell you that alternative energy is
low energy; the prodigious amounts of power
produced by fossil fuel technology cannot begin
to be matched by the ecological alternatives.
This means less energy available for use and,
consequently, the need for systems designed
for maximum efficiency.

The whole problem of energy efficiency is
put into perspective by a simple example: It has
been estimated that the average American family uses 300 kilowatt hours of electricity each
month. A 2000 watt wind-electric system
(costing over $6,000.00 on today's market) can
be expected to produce only about 100 kilowatt
hours of electricity per month in an area with a
10 mph average windspeed. If electrical appli-
ances were designed for maximum efficiency,
it is conceivable that our hypothetical family,
assuming a high degree of energy awareness,
could live quite well on one-third their accustomed consumption. However, when we realize
that the average deep freezer, to take only one
example, burns up 100 kilowatt hours per month,
we quickly realize that appliance efficiency has

a long way to go before we could comfortably begin to live within the energy budget provided by an ecologically adapted technology.

Too many people labor under the illusion that all they have to do is replace their present energy systems with a wind generator, solar panel or methane digester, and life will go on as it did before. Three generations of Americans have been so conditioned to receiving cheap energy by throwing switches and dialing thermostats that very few of us have the faintest conception of the tremendous forces required to produce even a small amount of usable power. The problem is succinctly put in Energy Primer (Portola Institute, 1974) when the authors state:

> "...It makes little sense to gear renewable energy systems to meet current high energy demands. The first step in assessing your needs is energy conservation. Make the distinction between your necessities and your luxuries. This does not mean that we must live in a primitive or totally austere way. It means that in measuring our needs we must first conserve what we have and then gear our needs to our resources ... not the other way around. We cannot apply renewable energy systems to fill present high energy demands and think that we are doing anything about the environment in which we live."

The implications of this deceptively simple statement are earth-shaking, for it calls for nothing less than a complete overhaul of the social and economic assumptions upon which our society is based. The most radical manifesto could not be as revolutionary.

This new American revolution, ironically being called for at the same time that the nation celebrates the bicentennial of its first revolt against tyranny, will be as much a revolt against the despotism of our own habits of thought and action as it is against their more obvious manifestations in corporate and governmental irresponsibility. A crucial question is: with communism as great an evil as capitalism, with what do we replace our prevailing economic and social frames of reference?

The Decentralist ideal of a civilization made up of autonomous agrarian communities is often advocated as a solution to our present problems, but what would it be like in actuality? Without some form of centralized control, it is not difficult to imagine the emergence of a petty provincialism not unlike the fuedal system of the Middle Ages: Oakland makes raids on San Francisco; the Duke of Chicago begins machinations for an alliance of all the Great Lakes fiefdoms to declare war against Cleveland; Arizona and New Mexico agree to cooperate in a scheme to exact tribute from all those who wish to travel and trade between Texas and California. While the examples are exaggerated, it is not difficult to imagine the problems a decentralized society would engender.

The roots of mankind's problems today (as always) are more moral and political than they are anything else. In Famine - Can We Survive?

(Ambassador College Press, 1974), an interesting statistic is presented:

"Around the world, only ten percent of the earth's 57 million square
miles of land is presently arable.
This makes for about one arable acre
per person. Another 20% of the earth's
land is permanent pasture land."

If we accept these figures as accurate, it
means that for every human on the planet,
three productive acres are available - one of
garden and two of pasture. In 1911, well before
"agribusiness" practices became widespread,
F. H. King in Farmers of Forty Centuries, made
the following observation about the intensive
organic farming techniques of the Far East:

"When we reflect upon the depleted fertility of our own older farm
lands, comparatively few of which
have seen a century's service, and
upon the enormous quantity of mineral fertilizers which are being applied annually to them in order to
secure paying yields, it becomes
evident that the time is here when
profound consideration should be
given to the practices the Mongolian
race has maintained through many
centuries, which permit it to be said
of China that one-sixth of an acre of
good land is ample for the maintenance of one person, and which are
feeding an average of three people
per acre of farm land in the three
southernmost of the four main is-
islands of Japan." (emphasis ours)

12

In abstract theory, then, it appears possible
to maintain between three and six times the current world population at an adequate nutritional
level by employing ecologically sophisticated,
highly intensive methods of agriculture.   To
achieve such a "utopian" end, however, would
require some very un-utopian means in the
form of a world dictatorship the likes of which
can only be imagined.

Utopian "solutions" to present problems
have always been with us, and always will, for
they are blueprints for the future - regardless
of how the builders may distort the architect's
original plans.   It is easy to criticize utopian
ideals as "impractical," "improbable," or
"naive," but without them, we'd have nothing to
measure our progress with.   The Declaration of
Independence, Constitution, and Bill of Rights
are all utopian documents, though we have yet
to achieve their promise.   If the world hates
the United States, it is not because of our stated
ideals, but because we don't live up to them.

No sophisticated individual, however, be-
lieves in the possibility of a present utopian
social order, although the achievability of a
utopian individual existence is as possible as
one wants to make it.   It is not in any individual's
power to change human nature, but it is within
every individual's power to change his own nature.
If the salvation of civilization is at all possible,
it begins with this.

To get from where we are now to where we
must go is a seemingly impossible step, in-
volving nothing less than an overnight change in

the way we perceive reality. For too long we
have either ignored or misunderstood the most
fundamental principles governing all life on this
earth, to the point that the faults of our ecologically invalid society can without exaggeration
be compared to the terminal illness of a nar-
cotics addict. In the months and years ahead
we shall have ample opportunity to observe how
our withdrawal symptoms will affect the planet.
If the patient manages to survive, it is to be
hoped that a healthier, more rational civilization may rise from the death bed it now inhabits.

II

It is not, however, within the scope of this
book to explore the almost insurmountable problems to be solved before our society could be
expected to function within an ecologically sane
frame of reference. Indeed, it is the author's
opinion that the last meaningful chance for a
societal change in this direction was passed
sometime just before World War II. At any
rate, survival is now an individual responsibi-
lity, and it is to individual solutions that this
book addresses itself.

The author, his wife and two children live
on a one-acre homestead in New Mexico's semi-
arid northern mountains. Inspired by F. H. King's
aforementioned 1911 book on oriental agricultural
practices, Farmers of Forty Centuries, (where-
in are described families of 12 people, plus

assorted livestock, supporting themselves on less than three acres of land), we are attempting to see if one acre of semi-desert can support four people without violating ecological principles. Far from repudiating technology, we believe that the key to survival lies in the enlightened use of an ecologically adapted technology. Just as the block and tackle, an extremely simple machine, makes use of natural laws to enable one man to lift by himself objects weighing many hundreds of pounds, an ecologically adapted technology can, by an analogous kind of "mechanical advantage," provide man with most of the amenities of civilization that he now receives at the expense of his environment.

The basic drive behind our research is to gain maximum energy output from a minimum input and drain on the environment. Although the law of entropy tells us that there can never be a gain without a certain percentage of loss, the primary aim of the alternative energy experimenter is to shave that percentage down to its irreducible minimum. Therefore, while we know that there aren't any "free" lunches, some lunches are considerably cheaper than others. When one reflects on the fact that current agribusiness practices in the United States require about twenty calories of energy in the form of petroleum to produce only one calorie of energy in the form of food, it becomes obvious that the connection between the petroleum industry and the supermarket is a lot closer than one might think. The entire process would be considerably more efficient if we could learn to drink our food directly from the gasoline pump!

The metaphor within which we seek these
alternatives is that of the eco-system. The
dictionary tells us that an eco-system is "an
ecological community considered together with
the non-living factors of its environment as a
unit." The key here is the phrase: as a unit -
the word eco-system doesn't so much describe
a thing as a dynamic process. This book describes our continuing experimentation with the
concept as applied to intensive food production
in a closed system.

The common definition of a desert is an
area with less than ten inches of annual rainfall,
and semi-arid environments are characterized
by yearly precipitation rates of between ten and
twenty inches. Our homestead in New Mexico,
at an elevation of 7000 feet above sea level, receives a yearly average of 11.76 inches of precipitation. Because of our fairly high altitude,
the annual mean temperature is about 47 degrees,
and it is only during June, July and August that
the monthly mean temperature rises above sixty
degrees. Thus, in an area with a growing season of little more than 90 days, we receive
barely 1.7 inches more rainfall than an area of-
ficially described as a desert. Even hard-
scrabble subsistence agriculture is difficult
here. In the old days, the local economy re-
volved around sheep and cattle ranching, though
in recent years this has fallen off sharply due
to overgrazing. These environmental factors
are generally typical of the Spanish villages in
northern New Mexico, and explain why the area
has remained relatively unspoiled by development. It was just this lack of exploitation which
made the area attractive to us, however, and
the harsh living conditions promised a natural

protection against much chance of it happening.
The main question was - could we survive in
such an unproductive area?

In the summertime, the only "reliable"
source of water comes from the village irrigation system. A mayor domo, or ditch boss, is
chosen each year to regulate the use of this
water - who gets how much, and when. In times
long past, the mayor domo was the most powerful man in the village - his word was law, and
woe betide anyone who took water out of turn;
but today, along with other symptoms of the
social breakdown of a once proud and self-suffi-
cient culture, near-anarchy characterizes the
regulation of irrigation water. In our village
the position of mayor domo has become something just short of ludicrous - he is effectively
unable to enforce anything, and the consequence
is a mad scramble to steal more water than the
neighbors.

Needless to say, it is extremely difficult
to raise even a subsistence crop under such
circumstances, and it was because of this that
we began casting about for alternatives. The
main questions were - how could we extend our
growing season, overcome the extreme scarcity
of water, and perhaps most importantly, free
ourselves from agricultural dependence upon
social factors over which we had no effective
control? The only restriction we placed on our
search was that the solution must be consistent
with ecological reality - only natural, non-polluting systems could be considered. Additional
requirements of our alternative system were:
maximum yields, minimum waste, and reasonable ease of operation and maintenance.

Gradually, the eco-system concept began to form in our minds. As it did, we began to realize that our problems were unique only in their particulars - most people are at the mercy of social and environmental factors over which they have little effective control. The eco-system idea seemed to promise an answer to problems much more important than those of only one family's survival in a less than perfect world.

Our original working unit, an underground greenhouse and aquaculture tank, was described in volume #28 of The Mother Earth News as follows:

"This is the first article in a series describing the construction and use of a complete 'eco-system' - an underground hydroponic greenhouse and aquaculture tank - powered by the wind, heated by the sun and fed on compost.

The unit, built on our small homestead in northern New Mexico (altitude 7,000 feet), is still in the experimental stages, but preliminary results have far surpassed our expectations...the greenhouse - four feet below ground level and banked with earth on the north side - utilizes a 1,400 gallon solar-heated catfish tank as a heat source for winter vegetable growing. A 12-volt, 200 watt Wincharger supplies the power to circulate the water through filters and a small flat-plate solar heat collector. The liquid in the fish tank acts as a 'heat battery,' collecting solar energy during the daytime and radiating it back into the greenhouse at night.

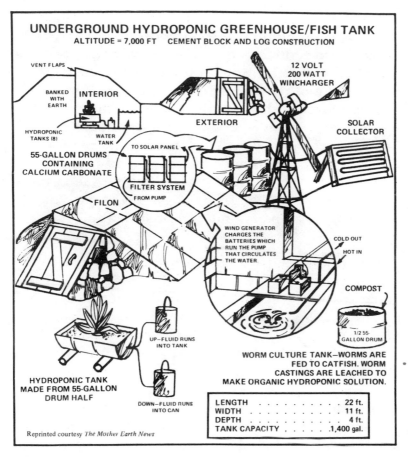

UNDERGROUND HYDROPONIC GREENHOUSE/FISH TANK

ALTITUDE = 7,000 FT   CEMENT BLOCK AND LOG CONSTRUCTION

VENT FLAPS

BANKED
WITH
EARTH

INTERIOR

12 VOLT
200 WATT
WINCHARGER

HYDROPONIC
TANKS (8)

WATER
TANK

EXTERIOR

SOLAR
COLLECTOR

55-GALLON DRUMS
CONTAINING
CALCIUM CARBONATE

TO SOLAR PANEL

FILTER SYSTEM

FROM PUMP

FILON

WIND GENERATOR
CHARGES THE
BATTERIES WHICH
RUN THE PUMP
THAT CIRCULATES
THE WATER.

COLD OUT

HOT IN

COMPOST

UP—FLUID RUNS
INTO TANK

1/2 55-
GALLON DRUM

WORM CULTURE TANK—WORMS ARE
FED TO CATFISH. WORM
CASTINGS ARE LEACHED TO
MAKE ORGANIC HYDROPONIC SOLUTION.

HYDROPONIC TANK
MADE FROM 55-GALLON
DRUM HALF

DOWN—FLUID RUNS
INTO CAN

LENGTH	22 ft.
WIDTH	11 ft.
DEPTH	4 ft.
TANK CAPACITY	1,400 gal.

Reprinted courtesy *The Mother Earth News*

Figure 1

The vegetables are grown hydroponically
in 55-gallon drums cut in half lengthwise
and filled with gravel.   Under the eight
hydroponic tanks are two additional drums
cut in half horizontally to make four compost bins in which earthworms are raised.
The worms are used to feed the catfish, and
the worm castings are leached to make the
organic hydroponic solution which feeds the
plants.

Our eco-system was designed to be almost completely self-sustaining. The wind generates the electricity which runs the water-circulating pump, the sun heats the water and the heated (and filtered) liquid keeps the fish happy and warms the greenhouse at night. The worms and their by-products provide food for fish and plants. The only substance that comes in from 'outside' is the organic matter which feeds the worms, and that from no farther away than our animal pens and compost heap... "

In theory, at least, we have created a self-sustaining eco-system: a basic food-producing unit capable of supplementing the diet of a small family. If hydroponic methods have the potential of more than tripling the harvest of agricultural crops, and if organic aquaculture can produce similar yields of animal protein, then it should be possible for any family or small community to produce a major portion of its nutritional requirements from a very small area of ground, in almost any environment - thus freeing them from the vicissitudes of moribund social and economic systems. As we shall see, the process isn't quite as simple as our original enthusiasm would have made it, and this book is a description of our on-going experience with the concept.

It should be emphasized at this point that a lot of people who should know better are still proselytising the myth of the free lunch - somehow we'll manage to feed the world with the vast quantities of food raised in our basement or rooftop mini-gardens. Aquaculture in particular seems prone to this sort of fantasy. We've heard of an individual who has applied for a $400,000.00 grant to show the world that anybody can raise cheap and abundant quantities of aquatic protein in their own backyard. We submit that for that kind of money one could raise fish on the moon, but no matter where they were raised it would undoubtedly be the most expensive seafood in the history of civilization. One sometimes hears the claim that a greenhouse of less than 200 square feet is capable of feeding a family of four. Since we have been guilty in the past of spreading such myths, we feel we have earned the right to call those who still make these claims either fools or liars, or both. With skill and proper management, greenhouses between 150 and 250 square feet, such as are described in this book, are capable of supplementing a large part of a family's diet, but by no means we know of, capable of providing all of it.

You won't find here a blueprint for the construction of a one-hundred percent efficient free lunch machine, but instead the description of an experiment in progress, including some educated opinions on how it might be improved. It should also be noted that, while the general features of our eco-system should be applicable almost anywhere, specific changes for environments drastically different from ours would be required. Obviously, our mini-eco-system is designed to function in response to the characteristics of the larger eco-system which surrounds it. High altitude, low temperatures and precipitation, and less than a ten-mile-an-hour average wind speed were but a few of the factors which had to be considered. Each area has its own natural characteristics which must be taken into consideration. For example, in areas which receive a heavy snowfall, a greenhouse would require a steeper-pitched roof than ours, and environments with less than an 8 mph wind speed average make wind-electric systems impractical.

It is unfortunate that in our era much of what passes for science is the exclusive province of a high priesthood of specialists who speak their own language and generally serve the interests of the demagogues who feed them. Science should ideally serve the legitimate needs of humanity within the framework of moral, humane and natural systems. The concepts and terminology of the ancient world seem, in many instances, to compliment such an ideal, though the biases of many contemporary "scientists" would make their immediate rejection mandatory. For example, we have divided the year into the Zodiacal Calendar because the solstices and equinoxes provide natural reference points much more appropriate to the yearly growing cycle than the arbitrary divisions of the Gregorian Calendar. One does not have to believe in astrology to accept the validity of this.

Basic research such as ours has traditionally been the province of universities and government. It seems that very few individuals feel that anything of consequence can even be conceived without a research grant of many thousands of dollars. Our greenhouse ecosystem was financed out of our own pockets and, in retrospect, we feel that it is just such independence at the grass-root level that is needed if the world is ever to evolve an ecologically adapted technology. We hope that, if nothing else, this book may serve as an inspiration to others to experience the tremendous satisfaction and confidence that comes with independence and self-sufficiency.

Photo 1

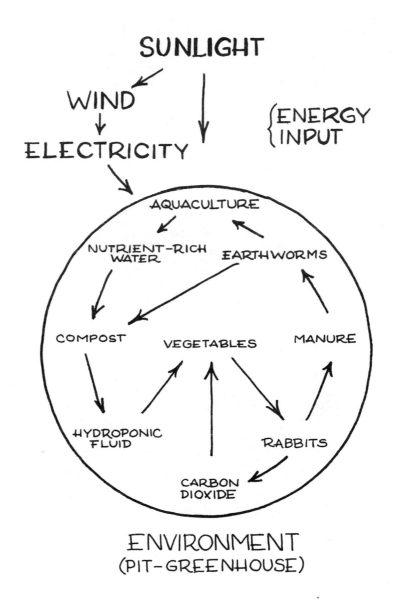

SUNLIGHT

WIND

{ENERGY
INPUT

ELECTRICITY

AQUACULTURE

NUTRIENT-RICH
WATER

EARTHWORMS

COMPOST

VEGETABLES

MANURE

HYDROPONIC
FLUID

RABBITS

CARBON
DIOXIDE

ENVIRONMENT
(PIT-GREENHOUSE)

Figure 2   Mandala for a greenhouse eco-system

GREENHOUSE BASICS

The different components of the eco-system are so interrelated that it is difficult to know where to start. Since the process is a continuous cycle of relationships, any given starting point is the "middle." However, since the greenhouse provides the environment within which our eco-system functions, that is where we shall begin.

Most of the literature refers to the greenhouse as a "forcing structure" - an artificial environment where plants can be "forced" to grow, even though the conditions outside the structure may be hostile to plant survival. Two of the many factors necessary for plant life are heat and light. The minimum requirements of any forcing structure are to retain warmth and allow light to enter, thus providing a "mini-environment" favorable to plant growth. The use of a forcing structure enables a gardener to increase his growing season from several weeks to the entire year, depending upon where he lives and the type of forcing structure he uses. The greenhouse, then, is designed in response to the light and temperature fluctuations in the yearly cycle of the seasons: if we all lived on the equator, forcing structures would be unnecessary.

We know that in the Northern Hemisphere the sun is at its zenith on the summer solstice - June 21st, and at its nadir on the winter solstice - December 21st - respectively, the longest and shortest days in the year. The midpoints, when the days and nights are of equal length, are the equinoxes - March 21st and September 21st. Each one of these four days in the year marks the beginning of a season - Summer and Winter on the solstices, Spring and Autumn on the equinoxes. Urban, technological man has become estranged from the significance of these very important dates in the yearly cycle, though pre-industrial and ancient cultures built their religious holidays around them. (In pre-Christian times, December 25th, our Christmas, marked the Saturnalia - a winter solstice celebration.)

Effective Growing Season

In working with the natural forces of our eco-system, we soon observed that the growing year really did seem to organize itself around the dates of the Zodiacal Calendar. If you can imagine each of the Zodiacal months as one hour in a 12-hour day, then dawn is the spring equinox and dusk is the autumnal equinox; noon and midnight are the solstices. Plant growth noticeably begins to fall off around the 21st of October - an "hour after sunset" in the yearly day, and it isn't until about the 21st of February, "one hour before dawn," that plant growth again seems to prosper. We wish to emphasize that we are not qualified to make any claims for or

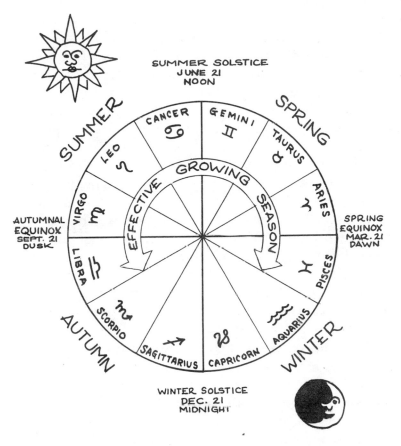

SUMMER SOLSTICE
JUNE 21
NOON

SUMMER

SPRING

CANCER

GEMINI

LEO

TAURUS

VIRGO

ARIES

GROWING SEASON

EFFECTIVE

AUTUMNAL
EQUINOX
SEPT. 21
DUSK

SPRING
EQUINOX
MAR. 21
DAWN

LIBRA

PISCES

SCORPIO

AQUARIUS

AUTUMN

SAGITTARIUS

CAPRICORN

WINTER

WINTER SOLSTICE
DEC. 21
MIDNIGHT

Figure 3

against astrology - we are merely using what,
for the purposes of greenhouse gardening in our
area, is an accurate and convenient frame of
reference to describe our experience.

When we speak of plant growth, we are
speaking of the process of photosynthesis - the
miracle by which green plants are able to draw
their essential energy directly from the sun.
The Encyclopedia Britannica gives us a capsule
definition: "Photosynthesis is the process by
which higher plants manufacture dry matter

through the aid of chlorophyll pigment, which uses solar energy to produce carbohydrates out of water and carbon dioxide. The overall efficiency of this critical process is somewhat low and its mechanics are extremely complex .... The amount of light, the carbon dioxide supply, and the temperature are the three most important environmental factors that directly affect the rate of photosynthesis; water and minerals in sufficient quantities also are necessary."

Greenhouses are designed to admit light and retain heat. If the temperature rises above or falls below certain limits, plant growth(photosynthesis) will cease. Similarly, if the intensity and duration of light does not meet certain minimum standards, growth is also checked. This latter factor is very important and seems not to be well understood by many people. The reason that the period from October 21st to February 21st produces minimal plant growth is because this is the period of the year in the Northern Hemisphere when the intensity and duration of light and heat are at their lowest levels. Maintaining adequate lighting in the winter greenhouse is a bit more complex than maintaining adequate temperature, so we will discuss it at length later on. For now, we'll confine ourselves to the greenhouse as a temperature-efficient structure.

Greenhouse Types

There are generally four different types of forcing structures - the cold frame, the hotbed, the greenhouse and the pit greenhouse. The cold frame is usually a small box-like structure with a removable glass cover. It is used to protect seedlings in the springtime, thus enabling a gardener to extend his growing season by several weeks. In effect, the cold frame is a very small, unheated greenhouse. The hot bed, on the other hand, is a cold frame with an auxiliary heat source. In the old days, hot beds utilized fresh manure as a source of heat - warmth given off by the composting manure kept the plants from freezing. In more recent times, electric wires embedded in the soil of the hotbed accomplish the same purpose at a far greater cost.

The word "greenhouse" itself conjures up the image, in most people's minds, of an above-ground, heated glass building used primarily for the propagation of flowers. This stereotype is generally correct, for greenhouses have historically been the playthings of the wealthy - places where ladies raise orchids for the envy and admiration of the local garden club. It is significant to note that virtually every available book on greenhouse gardening is devoted almost exclusively to flower-raising, and the literature which does deal with vegetable culture (usually tomatoes) is aimed at the huge commercial greenhouses which are invariably run along agribusiness lines. It seems that, up until now, those who could afford greenhouses could more than afford to buy their vegetables at the super-market, or else, in the case of commercial growers, were the ones actually supplying the supermarkets. At the time of this writing, there are no books we know of which deal exclusively with subsistence greenhouse vegetable gardening. Hopefully, this volume will help to fill that gap.

Just as the hotbed is a variation on the cold frame, the pit greenhouse is related in similar fashion to the "conventional" greenhouse. Ken Kern, in his book, The Ownerbuilt Homestead, informs us that:

"The oldest reported forcing structure in the U.S. was not a greenhouse as we know it today. It was, rather, a pit covered with glass on the south side, and earth insulation on the north. This so-called pit greenhouse was built into the side of a Waltham, Massachusetts hill around 1800..."

Photo 2   The Taylor/Gregg greenhouse (Photo courtesy of Kathryn Taylor)

America's first greenhouse, then, was a pit greenhouse, designed to take advantage of the insulation properties of the earth - certainly a more energy-efficient structure than a glass framework exposed on all sides to the weather, and requiring large in-puts of heat to keep its temperature up during the spring, fall and winter. The advent of cheap fossil fuels, however, made the latter type very popular, and nowadays, when the word "greenhouse" is mentioned, it is usually this sort of structure that is referred to.

Although pit greenhouses are rather rare these days, the concept of earth insulation for agricultural buildings has never really died out. Even America's first greenhouse is apparently still in operation. In Kathryn Taylor and Edith Gregg's 1969 book, Winter Flowers in Greenhouse and Sun-heated Pit, a most informative history of greenhouses is presented, along with photographs of the original Waltham, Mass. structure. They also describe the construction and use of their own simple pit greenhouse design. This structure is basically a pit dug into the ground with a peaked roof of glass built over it. (Photo 2)

The Lama Grow-hole

Our original introduction to the pit greenhouse came from the Lama Foundation's "grow-hole" poster, mentioned on page 59 of The Last Whole Earth Catalog. This structure (see Photo 3) was built several years ago - at an altitude of 8,000 feet - by the Lama commune on their land near Taos, New Mexico. It consists of an excavation dug into a south-facing slope, shored up and framed with timber, then covered with

Photo 3 The Lama Growhole

two layers of 16 mil plastic sheeting. The rationale behind this, and most pit greenhouses,
is that if the warmth of the sunlight falling on
the structure during the day can be retained
overnight then, ideally, no auxiliary source of
heat should be necessary. The Lama prototype
was an attempt to create this condition by using
the moist earth inside as a heat-collecting
"storage battery."

Some time after reading the Growhole Poster we visited another commune where a pit
greenhouse has been made from the cellar hole
of a burned-out ranch building. (Photo 4.) This
gave us the idea that a growhole doesn't necessarily have to be built into a hillside. (At that
time we hadn't seen Taylor & Gregg's book, so
were ignorant of their design.)

Photo 4   *Greenhouse made from cellar hole*

In the spring of 1972 we borrowed $100.00 and hired a backhoe to dig out a 12' X 24' hole in the ground.   For over a year the crater just sat there, with each rain or snowfall slowly

Construction of Our Pit Greenhouse

Photo 5   *Our hole*

filling it in again. Friends and neighbors were curious at first, then gradually ceased to mention the huge pit and accompanying pile of dirt which had become something of a local landmark. They were too polite to say so, but we knew that nobody thought anything would ever come of it.

We had enough money to continue construction in the late summer of 1973. By then we had become interested in aquaculture through the writings of John Todd and Bill McLarney of the New Alchemy Institute and - after conversations and correspondence with both researchers - decided that fish farming would have to be a part of our greenhouse. We'd also heard about the tremendous yields to be gotten from hydroponic gardening and were curious about the feasibility of developing an organic nutrient solution.

In early September we actually began building the greenhouse. The construction was simplicity itself and could easily be duplicated by anyone. The photographs tell the story.

Once we'd cleaned the hole of the dirt and debris accumulated over a year and a half, we poured a concrete footing as a base for the cement blocks. Desire to save on the expense of concrete made us decide not to lay a slab floor for the entire structure but just for the area beneath the fish tank. The floor of the greenhouse proper consists of three inches of coarse gravel.

The cement-block walls were laid up without mortar, the use of that material being a skill which doesn't come naturally to us and which tries our patience exceedingly. The mortarless method of cement-block laying is fast and simple: two courses of block are neatly stacked up, with the aid of string and plumb bob to make sure they're straight and square. The cement is carefully poured and tamped down every other hole. Wait for setting, and

Cement Blocks

Photo 6   The walls

you're ready for another course. Reinforcing rods are put in the openings at four-or-five-foot intervals to give the structure more strength. In this way, working rather leisurely two men built the greenhouse walls in just three days. (For this much concrete work a cement mixer is worth its weight in gold.)

The Fish Tank

The inside wall of the fish tank was also made of cement blocks, with every hole filled with concrete, and rebar placed at about 2-1/2 foot intervals to provide the strength needed to withstand water pressure. Please note, however, that this was a mistake and is not recommended. When the time came to fill the tank, it leaked like the proverbial sieve. There were just too many tiny holes for the water to run through. Only after plastering the inner surface with a stucco containing particles of fiberglas (sold under the trade name of Bloc-bond) and then painting a quarter-inch layer of hot tar on the sides and bottom did we finally stop the seepage. It would be much better to use slip forms and construct a tank with solid concrete walls.

Drainage

Of course, being four feet below ground level, a conventional drainage system was impractical. When it is necessary to empty the tank, the task is accomplished with a small wind-electric powered bilge pump. Because our part of the world is very dry, the necessity of keeping water out of the greenhouse proper has never arisen. Naturally, pit greenhouses should never be dug in areas subject to flooding, but for an occasional minor influx of water, a simple French drain should prove adequate. A French drain is essentially a gravel-filled sump which holds the water until it has had time to soak into the ground.

Penta

The main support for the roof framing was a 25-foot section of pine tree which we brought down from the nearby national forest. Smaller

pine poles and rough-cut 1 X 4 lumber complete
the framework which supports the fibreglas
roof. Again, we live in a semi-arid environment, and so wood-rot is not a problem here.
In areas with very high humidity, ordinary pine
would rot quickly in a greenhouse atmosphere.
Redwood has been the traditional greenhouse
lumber, though considering the increasing scarcity of this species, we cannot bring ourselves

Photo 7   Interior of greenhouse

to recommend it. We applied liberal quantities
of Penta to our wood. Though we were afraid that
this extremely toxic substance might kill every
living thing in the greenhouse, it didn't, and so
this wood preservative, if used with care and
intelligence, might provide the solution to wood-
rot problems in wetter climates than ours. More
potent than creosote, Penta is used to preserve
fenceposts. Although we haven't tried it, a coat

of Penta, followed by one or two coats of an asphalt paint, may be all the wood protection one would need. The asphalt paint would seal the Penta in where it couldn't come in contact with greenhouse plants or animals, yet the poison would still be available to kill any organisms which might attack the wood itself.

Photo 8   Ventilators

Cooling and Heating

Ventilator flaps were provided for use in the summer. We finished the basic structure in mid-October and even then got inside midday readings of 104° F. Such high temperatures are not desirable and we were glad to see the thermometer drop back down into the 80's when the vent flaps were all opened.

All greenhouses are placed within one of three separate temperature ranges - the <u>cool</u> greenhouse, with a range of 40° - 55° F.; the

moderate greenhouse at 55° - 65° F.; and the
warm greenhouse in the 65° - 75° F. range.
These figures represent minimum night time
temperatures - the lowest the greenhouse can
be allowed to go and still remain in its category.
Taylor and Gregg inform us that:

"The word 'greenhouse' originally
implied a cool greenhouse as differing
from a hothouse, or stove. In the old
books, plants requiring a high temperature were called 'stove' plants."

Obviously, each plant variety grows best
within a specific range of temperatures, and
since our version of the pit greenhouse does not
utilize fossil fuel for heat, it must be placed in
the cool greenhouse category. This puts a natural restriction on the kinds of plants we can
grow. Since we're interested only in the usual
North American vegetables, however, this
doesn't pose much of a problem - we never in-
tended to grow bananas in the first place.

Figure 4 shows the pertinent mean temperatures in our area for each of the Zodiacal
months of the 1973/74 year. As you can see, the
magical 40° F. low temperature does not appear
until Aries (March 21 - April 21). As previously
mentioned, however, we found that cool weather
plants (lettuce, spinach, etc.) began to thrive a
month earlier - around February 21st. The at-
tentive reader will also note that the mean temperature for Scorpio (October 21 - November 21)
is 41° F. - in theory a temperature capable of
providing another month of growing beyond the
October 21st "deadline." The fact that plant
growth is negligible during this period indicates
the effects of a waning photoperiod.

1974 GREENHOUSE DATA

	MONTH	Greenhouse Temperatures			Outside Temperatures		
		Low Average	High Average	Mean	Low Average	High Average	Mean
WINTER	Capricorn	30	58	44	15	51	33
WINTER	Aquarius	31	72	51	14	55	34
WINTER	Pisces	39	86	62	24	57	40
SPRING	Aries	40	94	67	26	59	42
SPRING	Taurus	49	99	74	37	73	55
SPRING	Gemini	55	99	77	46	82	64
SUMMER	Cancer	57	103	80	53	88	70
SUMMER	Leo	58	90	74	52	83	67
SUMMER	Virgo	57	90	73	47	80	63
AUTUMN	Libra	52	90	71	40	73	56
AUTUMN	Scorpio	41	80	60	28	67	47
AUTUMN	Sagittarius	29	73	51	16	64	40

ZODIACAL MONTHS

Capricorn = Dec./Jan.   Cancer = June/July
Aquarius = Jan./Feb.   Leo = July/Aug.
Pisces = Feb./Mar.   Virgo = Aug./Sept.
Aries = Mar./April   Libra = Sept./Oct.
Taurus = April/May   Scorpio = Oct./Nov.
Gemini = May/June   Sagittarius = Nov./Dec.

Figure 4

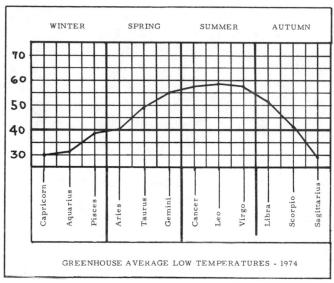

Figure 5

Ventilation

High greenhouse temperatures - anything
above 90° F. - are as much to be avoided as
temperatures below 40° F. In warm weather,
the greenhouse must be cooled. The conventional
greenhouse operator uses elaborate air condition-
ing equipment to accomplish this - all of it dependent upon fossil fuels. Since the eco-system
concept rules out such devices, we must rely on
natural methods only. Taylor and Gregg tell us
that:

"Temperature is dependent upon
ventilation. It is a matter of learning
to regulate the temperature by the degree of width to which the doors are
left open. One soon learns how different kinds of weather affect the pit. The
pit gardener develops almost as keen
a weather eye as a sailor; he is as dependent upon the sun as the real yachts-
man is upon the wind."

fans
on
top roof

With the above notable exception, writers of most greenhouse manuals generally recommend some kind of automated system. We have found that during hot weather the vents and the door can be left open all of the time without undue trauma to the plants. Actually, ventilation at this altitude is a problem only during two or three weeks in late June and early July. (During the Zodiacal month of Cancer.) We tried utilizing the heater-blower from an old Pontiac as an electric cool air ventilator which could be operated from the wind generator, but found that it was not powerful enough to affect more than a third of the greenhouse area. While it is true that the squash and tomatoes sometimes wilted during the heat of the day, so did their brothers and sisters outside in the garden. Be aware, also, that the greenhouse books are speaking of flowering plants, many of which are exotic tropical and semi-tropical varieties specific only to certain environments, and requiring a great deal of care. Our greenhouse plants are the homely tomatoes, cucumbers, squash and lettuce common to most gardens in the United States.

Shading

In addition to ventilation, shading the greenhouse will lower inside temperatures as much as ten degrees. Shading materials can range from simple tarpaulins and bamboo slats to strategically planted deciduous trees. (Leaves provide shade in the summer when it is required, and their absence during the colder part of the year allows the sun's rays to enter when they're most needed.) We even tried growing pole beans over the greenhouse (see cover photo), but found that they didn't grow quite fast enough

to shade the greenhouse during the hottest part
of the season.

While our high average greenhouse temperature for the month of Cancer, 1974, was a
stifling 103° F., the plants survived in good order, with no obvious deficiency symptoms other
than leaf wilting during the hottest part of each
day. The tomatoes and cucumbers seemed to
thrive in such an environment, though common
sense, plus all of the greenhouse books will tell
us that temperatures over 90° F. are not desirable. Although we did not make much use of
shading during 1974 and 1975, we intend to in
the future. Shading, plus natural ventilation,
should be sufficient to keep the greenhouse
reasonably cool during the summer.

Heating

In our experience, keeping the greenhouse
warm in cold weather has been more of a problem than keeping it cool in hot weather. It is a
fact that even the insulating properties of the
earth cannot keep the pit greenhouse free from
the freezing temperatures of mid-winter. Even
though our pit greenhouse is in the "cool" 40°
category, it has proven to be difficult to maintain even that relatively low temperature range
at night during certain times of the year.

Heating techniques for forcing structures
usually fall into two categories - insulation and
auxiliary sources of warmth. As mentioned,
most conventional greenhouses make use of
fossil fuels for winter heat - usually natural
gas, heating oil, or even electricity (the most
inefficient, in terms of energy, of all common
heating methods.)

The Wood Stove   Perhaps the simplest auxiliary heat source which doesn't burn non-renewable fuels is the wood-burning stove. In this regard, thermostatically controlled units, such as the Ashley automatic heater, would be the most efficient choice. The Waltham greenhouse designer's solution gives us some insight into how a pre-industrial society dealt with such problems. The bench upon which the plants grow is essentially an enormous flue. A fire is built at one end of this structure, and the warm gases and smoke pass under the plants on their way to the chimney at the other end of the greenhouse. Obviously a little experimentation with such a system would be required before the operator learned how to regulate the fire to be neither so hot as to burn the plants nor so cool as to allow them to freeze. Nevertheless, this method of greenhouse heating appears to be both simple and effective.

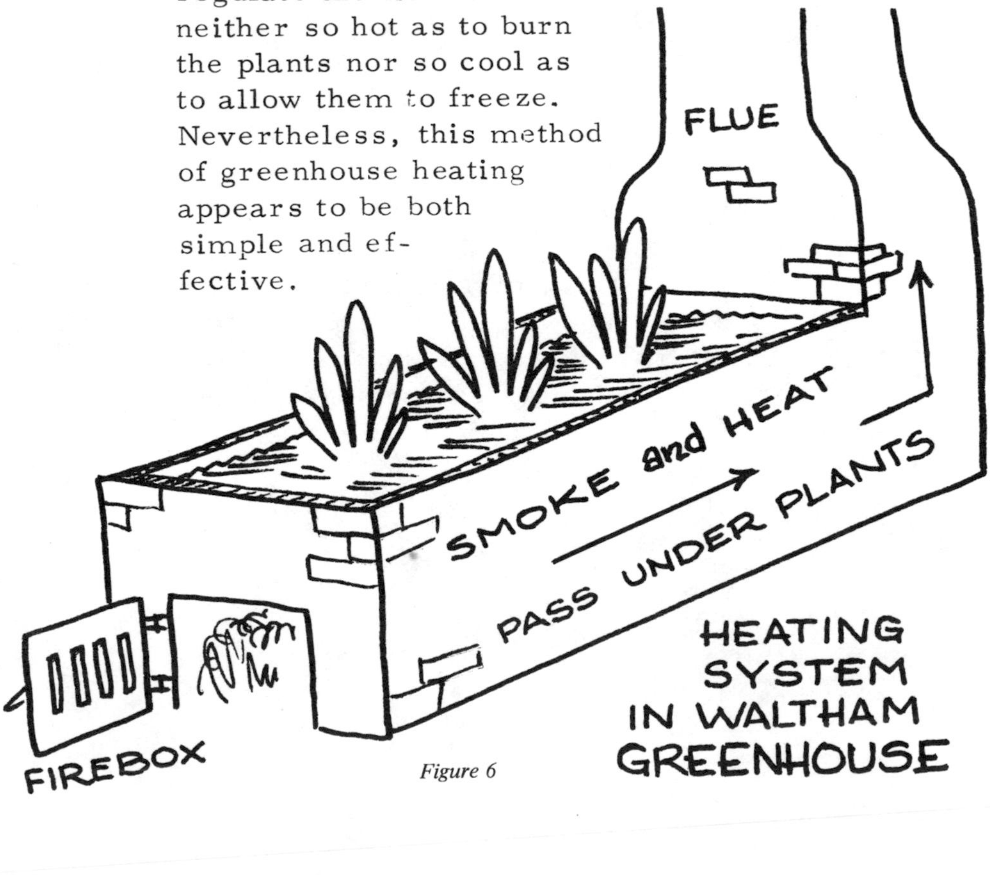

FLUE

SMOKE and HEAT

PASS UNDER PLANTS

HEATING SYSTEM IN WALTHAM GREENHOUSE

FIREBOX

Figure 6

Methods of insulation can take many different forms. To begin with, it is generally ac-
cepted that plastic-covered greenhouses are
significantly more efficient heat retainers than
glass-covered structures. It is further estimated that a double layer of plastic is up to 40%
more efficient than a single layer alone. The
Lama Foundation grow-hole made use of a
"plastic sandwich". This consisted of a layer
of aircap D-120 poly insulation (this is the plastic "bubble sheeting" commonly used as packing
material for shipping delicate merchandise)
sandwiched between two 16 mil sheets of vinyl
film.

While this kind of plastic is inexpensive
and readily available, its effective life is very
short - the material turns yellow and brittle
with age, and cannot be expected to last for
much more than one or two growing seasons. A
much better type of "plastic" is a special greenhouse material made of fibreglas, called Filon
or Lascolite. These are trade names - the
actual materials differ about as much as Fords
and Chevrolets (i.e. it's a matter of personal
preference which one you use). There are different types and thicknesses of this material,
some of it with a life expectancy of over fifteen
years. This is the covering we used - ours
came in three 4' X 24' rolls which we purchased
through the Sears catalog. We did not put it on
the greenhouse in a double layer, however.
During the 1974 cold season we put up a sheet of
the much cheaper vinyl plastic on the inside -
this was an experiment to determine the effectiveness of the doubled layer. During 1975 we

45

did not use the vinyl inside, and were thereby convinced of its effectiveness - the mean low temperatures in Capricorn and Aquarius were 30° and 31° F. degrees respectively. During the same period in 1975 the mean low temperatures were 22° F. and 27° F. without the extra layer of plastic - a difference of between 4 and 8 degrees. Double-layering, then, is definitely worth the extra trouble and expense.

Insulation can take many different forms other than the double-layer. The Taylor and Gregg pit greenhouse doesn't make use of either double-paned glass or auxiliary heat, relying instead on insulation panels which are placed over the glass in the evenings and removed each morning - except, of course, during periods of inclement weather when the insulation is left on. These insulation "panels" need be nothing more elaborate than burlap sacks full of leaves. We can attest to the tremendous difference that a few inches of insulation can make in greenhouse heat retention. During the coldest part of the winter of 1974 the temperature plunged to 5° below zero one night. The inside greenhouse temperature was a balmy 34° F. - entering the structure that morning was like stepping into a heated room. The reason was ten inches of snow on the greenhouse roof - a very effective insulator.

The efficient use of both double-paned glass or plastic in conjunction with insulation panels should enable the pit greenhouse operator to maintain the winter mean low temperature at or above the magic 40° F. required for the cool greenhouse. In the future we will construct

solar collector's amount = energy

46

removable plastic-covered frames which can
be easily mounted inside the greenhouse. (It
may not be desirable to have a permanent double
layer, since it could make summertime temperatures unmanageably hot.) In addition, we will
have insulation panels for placement on the outside of the greenhouse at night and when the
weather is cloudy.

The Passive System

There is another category of greenhouse
heating which doesn't naturally fall under either
insulation or auxiliary heat - it might most accurately be labeled as the "passive system."
This is the utilization of a heat storage system
such as water or rocks to hold the high daytime
temperatures overnight. In our greenhouse,
the high mean temperatures for Capricorn and
Aquarius were 58° F. and 72° F. - well above
the 40° F. minimum we needed. Even in mid-
winter the greenhouse gets quite warm during
the day - the question is, how can we keep that
warmth from dissipating after sunset?

Some solar houses, as well as greenhouses,
utilize 55-gallon drums of water (painted black
to absorb heat) as passive storage systems.
While this makes good sense for a solar-heated
dwelling, in a greenhouse an aquaculture tank
serves the same purpose while also providing
the environment for another food source.

The original plan for our eco-system called
for a solar panel through which the fish tank
water would be circulated - the solar energy
thus picked up during the day would, in theory,
provide heat at night. Water is an extremely
efficient heat storage medium, and the rationale

Photo 9   Solar panel

was that if the water temperature could be maintained at a high enough level, the greenhouse
could be kept above 40° F., even in midwinter.
The idea is a sound one, but we found that for
it to work, a solar collector of at least one-
hundred square feet would be required to keep
the 1400-gallon tank at an effective temperature.
At the time of this writing, commercially available solar panels cost between $4.50 and $12.00
per square foot. By the time it was installed,
a 100-square foot solar collector would cost between $500.00 and $1300.00 - a price not only
beyond our means, but incompatible with our
objective of keeping the eco-system within the
reach of those who need it most.

Although we could build our own collector
for far less money, we soon came upon another
limiting factor which made that solution imprac-

tical. The 12-volt, 66 watt bilge pump used to circulate the fish tank water is not nearly powerful enough to push liquid through 100 square feet of solar collector. A pump large enough to handle the job would require much more power than the monthly 20 kilowatt hour maximum that can theoretically be expected from the wind-electric system we are now using. To provide an "off the shelf" wind and solar energy package adequate to these needs would cost far in excess of a conventional greenhouse heating system. While the aesthetics of using such alternative energy systems are very appealing, the economics are against us. Since fossil fuel technology is not to be considered, we must find other solutions to the problem of maintaining the greenhouse at a minimum temperature of 40° F. As already mentioned, the use of a double layer of plastic in addition to outside insulation panels, would go a long way toward solving this problem, if not solve it altogether.

The Plastic Tent

During the latter part of the winter of 1975, we constructed a plastic-covered framework over two of our hydroponic tanks - in effect, creating a cold frame inside the greenhouse. Actually, it was more like a hotbed, because each night we kept a burning kerosene lamp inside the structure to insure the plants wouldn't freeze. The relatively small enclosure held heat very well, some nights not going below 68°F. While we were "cheating" by using kerosene, a large candle would have served as well. This took care of the heat problem.

There are factors other than temperature which must be considered, however, if we can expect to raise many vegetables in the winter-time.

Figure 7   The plastic tent

PHOTOPERIOD

In late summer have you ever noticed that the leaves of certain trees begin changing to their autumn colors before the first frost? At the time of this writing, Sept. 4, 1975, the leaves on the locust trees in our yard are beginning to turn yellow, though our first frost of the season has yet to occur. This phenomenon illustrates the effects of a waning photoperiod - the amount of light which is available for the plant to carry out its primary function of photosynthesis. Some plant species are so specialized in their light requirements that even one less hour of sunlight per day will trigger the beginning of their dormant cycle.

Regarding winter photoperiods, Ernest Chabot, in his book Greenhouse Gardening for Everyone, one of the few general greenhouse manuals that discusses vegetable growing, states:

"Perhaps you're asking, 'why not grow these fruits under glass in winter as well as summer?' Of course you can, but the expense for additional heat and the slow production when days are short would hardly make them profitable in a small greenhouse."

Canadian agricultural bulletin #1460, Soilless Culture of Commercial Greenhouse Tomatoes, tells us that:

"The fall crop is harvested in October, November, and early December. Production beyond this date is not economical owing to high costs of heating, insufficient daylight, and slow development and ripening of fruit."

Cathey and Campbell, in "Lamps and Lighting - a horticultural view," an article appearing in the November 1974 issue of Lighting Design and Application, explain further:

"In the winter, most plants in greenhouses in northern latitudes do not receive enough light to maintain the growth characteristics that are possible during the rest of the year. Limitation of light reduces the photosynthetic activity of the plants."

The reason we have quoted at length on this subject is to emphasize something that many people do not take into consideration - we all know that greenhouses must be kept warm in the wintertime, but relatively few of us consider the problem of insufficient light when the days are short.

Another glance at Fig. 3 reminds us that
the effective growing season ends October 21st,
and doesn't begin again until somewhere around
the 21st of February. The limiting factors are
both temperature and photoperiod. Thus, even
if it is possible to maintain sufficient heat in the
greenhouse during the winter, plant growth will
still be inadequate because of the lack of available light.

Wittwer and Honma in Greenhouse Tomatoes
- Guidelines for Successful Production go so far
as to say:

> "... The technology for maintaining
> a greenhouse tomato crop in which
> harvest begins in the fall and continues
> at a profitable level of productivity
> through the winter is not yet available."

If even commercial growers with "efficient"
fossil fuel heating and lighting systems consider
winter greenhouse production to be uneconomical,
how can we, with only the low energy of the natural systems available to us, expect to make it
a worthwhile endeavor? Realistically, it may
not be feasible, but there are a few possibilities
to be explored before a final decision can be
made.

Three Qualities of Light

There are three qualities of light which are
important for us to consider. All three act together to facilitate efficient plant growth; they
are:
1. Intensity of light;
2. Duration of light;
3. Spectral content of light.

lights from Lilly

The intensity of sunlight is at its lowest in winter because the low angle of the sun causes its energy to pass obliquely through the atmosphere. Dust in the atmosphere screens out a tremendous amount of energy. Because of the sun's lower winter angle, the days are shorter, affecting light duration. The spectral content, of course, remains the same.

Light Intensity

Light intensity can be substantially increased by placing reflectors behind the plants. We proved this to ourselves during the early spring of 1975, when we placed a board covered with aluminum foil behind some Chinese cabbage seedlings. Another group of identical seedlings had no reflector. Within one week the seedlings receiving the additional reflected light were measurably larger than the control group. With-

Photo 10   Early Spring Greenhouse

in two weeks, the difference in the sizes of the two groups of plants was enough to suggest that they had been planted several weeks apart!

There is a point of diminishing returns on the use of reflected light, however. This was reached later in the season when other plants started with reflectors showed no differences from those without them. The explanation for this phenomenon is quoted from the Encyclopedia Britannica:

> "Over a range of moderate temperatures and at low to medium light intensities (relative to the normal range of the plant species), the rate of photosynthesis increases as the (light) intensity increases and is independent of temperature. As the light intensity increases to higher levels, however, the rate becomes increasingly dependent upon temperature and less dependent upon intensity; light "saturation" is achieved at a specific light intensity, and the rate then is dependent only on temperature if all other factors are constant."

This explains why plant growth after February 21st suddenly begins to prosper, even though the greenhouse temperatures are still relatively low: the days have gotten long enough so that light intensity and duration are within the range of the plants' photoperiodic response.

Light Duration

Reflectors, of course, only increase light intensity, not duration. Therefore, in midwinter a reflector alone is not enough to bring

plant growth up to normal. What is needed is
a means of extending the short winter day to a
length at least equal to a summer day.

The following table of photoperiods shows
the day lengths on the solstices and equinoxes
in four United States latitudes:

PHOTOPERIODS IN THE UNITED STATES			
	Winter (Dec. 21)	Spring (Mar. 21) Autumn (Sept. 21)	Summer (June 21)
(1) 45° N. Latitude	8 hrs 46 min	12 hrs 17 min	15 hrs 37 min
(2) 40° N. Latitude	9 hrs 20 min	12 hrs 15 min	15 hrs 1 min
(3) 35° N. Latitude	9 hrs 48 min	12 hrs 14 min	14 hrs 31 min
(4) 30° N. Latitude	10 hrs 13 min	12 hrs 12 min	14 hrs 5 min

    (1) 45° N. Lat. = Portland, Ore; Minneapolis; Bangor
    (2) 40° N. Lat. = Salt Lake City; Denver; Philadelphia
    (3) 35° N. Lat. = Santa Barbara; Albuquerque; Memphis
    (4) 30° N. Lat. = Houston; New Orleans; Jacksonville

Figure 8

At our location, roughly 35° N. Latitude,
we receive a little less than ten hours of daylight on December 21st, the winter solstice.
Since we know that our effective growing season
ends around the 21st of October, we can inter-
polate from the table that any day-length of less
than eleven hours is inadequate for proper plant
growth. The intensity and duration of light is
below the level of photoperiodic response that
millions of years of evolution have built into
most of the vegetables we are interested in
raising. Plants evolved in the natural world,
not in greenhouses, and we must provide them
with the environmental conditions they require
if we expect to grow much food during the "night-
time" portion of the yearly cycle.

While light intensity may be boosted with reflectors, light duration can only be increased by using an artificial light source such as fluorescent tubes. Since we know that a winter day at our latitude is about ten hours long, and a summer day is about fourteen hours long, we would only need to burn lights for a total of four hours a day during December to give the plants the photoperiodic equivalent of a day in June. This could easily be accomplished with a timing device which would turn the lights on two hours before sunrise, off at dawn, and on again for two more hours after sunset.

Wind Electric Power

Since our eco-system is dependent upon the wind for its source of electricity, we must first understand the unique characteristics of wind-electric systems before we can assess their practicality as a power source for artificial lighting in the winter greenhouse.

The wind has been one of man's oldest sources of energy, and in the impending era of energy shortages it will undoubtedly again play an important role. Like most natural energy sources, however, it is not capable of providing the prodigious amounts of electricity that modern technological man is accustomed to using every day. To understand why this is so, perhaps a good place to begin is a discussion of the basic facts of electricity.

Volts, Amps & Watts

The three most important units of electrical measurement which concern us are: volts, amperes (amps) and watts. The easiest way to remember the difference between amps and volts is to think of amps as "current" which is measured in much the same way as the volume of water in a pipe is measured. If amps are volume, then volts can be thought of as "pressure" - the amount of push behind the volume of water. There's a world of difference between the flow of a swift mountain brook (high voltage, low amperage), and the flow of the sluggish waters of a large, slow-moving river (high amperage, low voltage). The analogy is not a perfect one, but it gives you the idea.

Obviously, the relationship between amps and volts is very important - the combination of the two when multiplied together is the total amount of electricity available, and is measured in watts. Volts times amps equals watts. Thus, the electric volume of one ampere under the pressure of one volt means that one watt of power is available to do work. A 40 volt wind generator designed to produce 70 amps at full output is rated as a 2800 watt machine (40X70 = 2800). Since watts are the measure of available power, the very first thing that should concern us when considering a wind generator is: how many watts is it capable of producing? The easiest way to visualize the potential output of any given generator is to imagine the number of 100 watt light bulbs it can theoretically light up at once. A 200 watt generator will light only two 100 watt bulbs, while a 3000 watt generator will light thirty of them.

The Kilowatt Hour

Since the watt is a relatively small unit of power, electricity is usually described in terms of the "kilowatt" - a block of energy consisting of 1000 watts. Even this term is relatively meaningless, however, unless it can be related to

time. Thus, a kilowatt hour is the use of a given
unit of electric power (one kilowatt) in relation
to a given unit of time (one hour). 1000 watts
used for one hour is equal to one kilowatt hour.
Five-hundred watts used for two hours still adds
up to one kilowatt hour, as does one watt for
1000 hours or 2000 watts for one-half hour.

> "Supplemental illumination in
> greenhouses increases photosyn-
> thesis. Cost of power, however,
> makes this impractical for all but
> crops of the highest value. Fluo-
> rescent lights are the most effi-
> cient for photosynthesis."
>
> Encyclopedia Britannica

The electric company bases your monthly
bill on the number of kilowatt hours you use
during that period. If, during one month's
time, you only burned a single 100 watt bulb for
a total of ten hours, you would be charged for
100 watts times 10 hours, or one kilowatt hour.
(The electric meter automatically adds up the
total number of kilowatt hours used.) Of course,
this example is used only for the purpose of
illustration - in actuality, there is a minimum
charge each month which is based on much more
than one kilowatt hour.

The number of kilowatt hours which a given
wind-electric system can produce each month
is related to generator/battery capacity, the
size of the propeller, and the average wind
speed at its location. One could purchase the
largest, most powerful wind generator made
and it would be worthless if the average wind
speed was inadequate. Even a Rolls Royce is
only an expensive chunk of iron if there is no
gasoline available to run it.

Average
Wind Speed

Ideally, before installing any wind-electric
system, one should take careful measurements
with an anemometer to determine the average
wind speed for the area in which the installation
is being made. In actuality, few people do this.
The more sophisticated anemometers are relatively expensive instruments, and the inexpensive, hand-held models require the dedicated
observer to go out when the wind is blowing,
climb to some high and unobstructed "platform"
(such as the roof of the house) and take daily
readings. It has always seemed to us that to
obtain a truly accurate record by this method,
one would have to spend all his time up on the
ridgepole watching the anemometer.

Often the average wind speed of a region
can be estimated fairly accurately by comparing
local conditions with those at the nearest airport or weather station. In our case, the average wind speed at the Albuquerque Municipal
Airport (over 150 miles away) for the period
1951-1960 was 8.6 mph. The wind speed average
for the Santa Fe Municipal Airport (70 miles
away) for the years 1946-1974 was 11.3 mph.
(This figure given by the Dept. of the Air Force

Weather Service.) The U.S. Weather Bureau, however, states that the Santa Fe "wind velocities are light, averaging only seven miles per hour for the year."

We estimated our local average wind speed to be "at least" 10 mph because the air always seems to be in motion here. During the spring months the wind often blows at near gale force for days at a time. Admittedly, this isn't a very accurate method of estimating average wind speed. After all, you could theoretically come up with a 10 mph average if you lived in an area where the wind blew 120 mph in March and zero mph for the other 11 months. We feel that we may have seriously overestimated our average wind speed. Enthusiasm for an alternative source of power got us deeply involved in wind-electric systems before we fully understood the many complex variables which must be considered.

Yearly "average" wind speed, of course, is the sum of the mean wind speeds for each month divided by 12. "Average" can be a relatively meaningless term in July and August when the potential wind energy is at its lowest ebb in the Northern Hemisphere. Unless your own patch of North America is unusual in its geographical or climatic features, you'll find that mid-summer is the least windy time of the year. Nevertheless, determining your local average wind speed is still the single most important method you can use to ascertain the practicality of a wind-electric system in your area. Michael Hackleman, in his book Wind and Windspinners, gives us an important rule of thumb to guide us in this decision:

"Below 8 mph average wind speed, consider three times carefully before investing much money in a wind-electric system. From 8-10 mph average, look twice; from 10-12 mph average, move on it; and from 15-20 mph average, why don't you already have a wind system?"

Our Wind Electric System

Because we wanted our eco-system to be capable of easy duplication by anyone who wanted to build one, we chose the relatively inexpensive and only readily available wind generator still manufactured in the United States: the Model 1222-H Wincharger. This 12 volt, 200 watt machine is available from Dyna Technology, Inc., P.O. Box 3263, Sioux City, Iowa 51102.

The specifications for this unit state that it will produce 20 kilowatt hours of electricity per month in areas with an average wind speed of 10 mph. Since we have no reason to doubt the manufacturer's specifications, we have, by the rather expensive method of using the wind generator as an "electric anemometer," determined that our yearly average wind speed falls somewhere in the 8-10 mph category. In other words, we are not getting a full 20 kwh/month average - certainly not during the summer months. In the absence of instrumentation to record it, we can only estimate; we are probably getting somewhere between 15 and 20 kilowatt hours per month, although during March, April and May (our windiest months) we may be getting as much as 26 kwh/month. When compared with the 300/kwh/month used by the average American family, 20 kwh/month is an almost insignificant amount of power. The ecosystem, however, is dedicated to getting maximum output from the relatively small input of natural energy sources. Obviously, we must make every watt count.

Fluorescent Lighting

In terms of increasing photoperiod in the winter greenhouse, the energy efficiency of the fluorescent tube, plus the fact that it produces wave-lengths which are beneficial to plant growth, make it ideal for our purposes. It is a happy fact that, watt for watt, fluorescent tubes emit more than twice the amount of light that incandescents do. The heat output is about the same, but since the heat is spread over such a large area the total effect is one of "coolness." This enables us to put fluorescent lights very close to the plants without danger of burning them.

Most fluorescent light gardeners use a standard fixture of four 40-watt tubes, which draws 160 watts (4X40 = 160). Using 160 watts for four hours (the length of time to bring our photoperiod to the equivalent of a day in June) equals 640 watt-hours of power used each day (160 X 4 = 640). If the lights are used at this rate for a month, we will consume 19.2 kilowatt hours every 30 days (640 X 30 = 19200). We know that our particular wind-electric system will create 20 kwh of electricity a month in an area with a 10 mph average wind speed, so it should easily be able to provide the 19.2 kwh/mo we need - assuming we had a 10 mph wind speed, that is! Since we have something less than that, we'll be taxing our system to its limit if we burn the lights four hours a day.

Other Wind Electric Systems

Of course, all of this data is based on a specific wind-electric system - the M-1222 H Wincharger. A larger system would produce much more power. For example, a Dunlite 115 volt, 2000 watt system should produce 80 kwh/ month or more in an area like ours. Unfortunately, at the time of this writing, Dunlite (Australian) and Electro (Swiss) wind electric systems (two of the most popular high wattage units available on today's market) are priced many thousands of dollars above the budgets of most of us. The old American-made Jacobs and Wincharger high wattage machines, which were popular on farms and homesteads in this country before Rural Electrification, are becoming increasingly scarce, as more and more alternative energy enthusiasts are buying them up at higher and higher prices. The cheapest and most practical way of getting a higher electrical output is to construct your own generator - assuming that you have the tools and skills required for such a project. The author has written a chapter on the construction of a home-built unit (capable of up to 4800 watts output) which appears in the book, Producing Your Own Power, (Rodale Press,1974) For readers interested in constructing their own machine, we have included that chapter in the appendix to this book. The electricity produced by such a unit should be more than sufficient to power both lights for winter growing and a pump big enough to make the original solar heating concept practical.

We are, however, using a relatively low-powered unit at the present time - how can we increase the winter photoperiod under our current circumstances without running the risk of constantly draining the batteries? Since we have not yet used lights in the greenhouse, we can only outline some possible solutions.

Other Fluorescent Possibilities

Three 40-watt fluorescent tubes used according to the afore-mentioned schedule would only draw 14.4 kwh/month, and two tubes only 9.6 kwh. Of course, each tube subtracted from service reduces the light intensity, but if used in conjunction with reflectors behind and beneath the plant, the loss could be minimized. There is evidence to indicate that plants are able to respond to light from beneath their leaves as well as from above; thus, a tinfoil "mulch" around each plant would reflect light up under the leaves for increased intensity.

Light intensity is measured in foot-candles, and it is important that the tubes be placed close enough to the plant to provide the proper strength of illumination. Since fluorescent tubes are relatively cool, they can be put within four inches or less of the plants without danger of burning them. Most writers seem in agreement that a light intensity of at least 1000 foot-candles is best for maximum growth. The following chart, taken from The Encyclopedia of Organic Gardening (Rodale, 1972), gives the foot-candle to plant distance ratios for two standard 40-watt tubes with a reflector at the light source:

1	inch from lights			1,000	foot candles	
2	"	"	"	950	"	"
3	"	"	"	750	"	"
4	"	"	"	650	"	"
5	"	"	"	560	"	"
6	"	"	"	460	"	"
7	"	"	"	430	"	"
8	"	"	"	370	"	"
9	"	"	"	360	"	"
10	"	"	"	350	"	"

Figure 9

Of course, since light intensity varies inversely with the square of the distance from the source, a small change in light distance from the plants will make a large change in the number of foot-candles received.

Grow-lights

At this point we should mention that special fluorescent "grow-lights" are available at a higher price than conventional tubes, but they apparently offer no significant advantages. In our research on the subject we have found that most experts recommend a half and half combination of "warm white" and "cool white" tubes. The extra expense of the special grow-lights is not commensurate with their plant growing ability.

Spectral Content of Light

As briefly mentioned before, the spectral content of light is very important to proper plant growth. We know that white light is made up of all of the colors of the spectrum, and that each color is distinguished by its own wave length. These wave lengths of light are measured in angstrom units - one angstrom unit being one-hundred-millionth of a centimeter long. Scientists have determined that plants particularly respond to red light at 6500 angstrom units, and to blue light at 4500 angstrom units. The red end of the spectrum promotes flowering in plants, and the blue end is necessary for foliage growth. Generally, fluorescent tubes are high in blue light, and incandescent bulbs are high in red light.

Many artificial light gardeners mix fluorescent and incandescent illumination to provide a balance of both red and blue light. Used as a supplement to daylight in the winter greenhouse, however, fluorescent tubes alone should be adequate. This is because the winter greenhouse crop should logically consist of cool-weather plants such as lettuce, spinach, Swiss chard, Chinese cabbage, etc. - plants which are grown for their foliage rather than their fruit. Warm weather crops - those generally raised for their fruits, such as tomatoes, cucumbers, squash, etc. - cannot be grown efficiently in an unheated eco-system greenhouse during the winter because they require minimum temperatures of 60° F. Since red light is most necessary to fruit-producing plants, it need not concern us too much - we want all the blue light we can get to increase the foliage on our winter lettuce and spinach. Actually, a mixture of warm-white and cool-white fluorescent tubes should provide an adequate balance of red and blue wave-lengths. (Experiments with blue and red filters placed over a large growing space to alter the color of daylight may have interesting results. We have not yet tried this idea, but intend to do so in the future.)

Cyclic Lighting   Cathey and Campbell, in the publication cited earlier, mention some very interesting experiments with photoperiod control which have tremendous implications for those of us restricted to the relatively low power output provided by alternate energy systems. We have not yet tried these methods, so mention them here only to acquaint the reader with their existence:

> "Techniques were developed in the late fifties to reduce the electrical energy requirements for photoperiod control... The technique was based on repeating light-dark cycles over several hours during the middle of a long night... We have observed that 10 to 20 foot-candles from incandescent-filament lamps, 30 seconds on and 30 seconds off all night, promoted the early flowering of china aster, Hyo-scyamus, Petunia, snapdragon, sugar-beet, and tuberous-rooted begonia.

The use of artificial light to promote
the continued vegetative growth of
woody plants is relatively easy to obtain with cyclic lighting... It means
that three minutes of light every 30
minutes or six seconds every 60
seconds for the middle four hours of
a 16-hour dark period promote the
continued vegetative growth of most
woody plants. "

As is usual in much of the greenhouse literature, flowers and ornamentals are the plant
types most often referred to, so it appears that
there is much research yet to be done with vegetable crops. The results of the above techniques are very promising, however, and the
energy efficiency of cyclic lighting just may be
the key to making winter greenhouse gardening
economical.

If a 4 tube, 160 watt fluorescent fixture was
turned on for fifteen minutes every hour during
the middle four hours of the winter night (a
simple timer could accomplish this), only 160
watt-hours would be consumed each day. This
adds up to only 4.8 kilowatt hours every 30 days
- a relatively insignificant amount of electricity,
even by wind-electric standards. The reader is
also asked to note that some of the light intensities in the above experiments were as low as
ten foot-candles - 100 times less intense than
the 1000 foot-candles recommended by most
artificial light gardening manuals. Again, we
have not yet begun our experiments with cyclic
lighting, but the technique appears to hold much
promise.

Adequate temperature and photoperiod are only two of the requirements that plants need for carrying out photosynthesis. Carbon dioxide is a third necessity that is often overlooked by greenhouse gardeners.

CARBON DIOXIDE

Earlier we quoted a phrase from the Encyclopedia Britannica; to give ourselves a point of
departure for this section, it bears repeating:

"The amount of light, the carbon
dioxide supply, and the temperature
are the three most important factors
that directly affect the rate of photosynthesis; water and minerals in sufficient quantities also are necessary."

We have briefly covered temperature and
photoperiod as factors to be considered in greenhouse gardening, and the subject of water and
minerals will be discussed later in the section
on hydroponics. At this point we want to exam-
ine the important role played by carbon dioxide
in plant growth.

**The Most
Important
"Fertilizer"**

Almost everyone knows that the gas that we
breathe in is called oxygen (O_2), and it is essential to all life. What many people may not know,
or have forgotten, is that the gas we breathe
out is called carbon dioxide (CO_2), and it is no

less essential to all life, since it is a vital ingredient used by plants in photosynthesis. Animal forms, from bacteria to man produce carbon dioxide through the process of respiration. (It is also produced in other ways, but for the purposes of the eco-system greenhouse we are primarily interested in carbon dioxide as a product of the respiration of higher animals and of the micro-organisms which produce compost.)

The normal concentration of carbon dioxide in the atmosphere is only 300 parts per million, yet from this relatively meagre supply plants are able to grow and carry on all their vital functions. One explanation for the tremendous explosion of plant growth in the Coal Age is that the earth's atmosphere during that period contained more carbon dioxide than it does now. Plants grew faster than they were consumed, and the result was the creation of our present supply of coal, oil and gas - the so-called fossil fuels that we are now running out of. Just as the electro-chemical energy manifested in your brain cells as you read these words was recently solar energy "fixed" by the process of photosynthesis in plants, so is the energy that powers your automobile as you drive to the corner store for a pack of cigarettes a manifestation of sunlight that was beamed on the earth about 250 million years ago. The fact that increased levels of carbon dioxide in the atmosphere produced such an abundance of plant growth during the days of the dinosaurs gives us an important clue as to how we can increase the yield of our greenhouse crops today. Wittwer and Honma in Greenhouse Tomatoes - Guidelines for Successful Production, tell us that:

"Carbon dioxide has produced the
most spectacular yield increases of
any growth factor yet discovered in
the culture of greenhouse crops...
Under some conditions, the most limiting factor in the growth of terrestrial
plants is the carbon dioxide concentration in the atmosphere. This is particularly true for greenhouse crops since
the carbon dioxide level in the enclosed
atmosphere is often depleted far below
that of the 300 ppm in the outside air..
The increases in fruit yields range
from ten to seventy per cent, with
averages of from fifteen to fifty-five
percent... The response to carbon
dioxide occurs over a wide range of
light intensities. It is possible to com-
pensate partially for low light intensities such as occur on cloudy days
by adding carbon dioxide to the atmos-
here."   (Emphasis ours)

"The air contains only about (300
parts per million) of carbon dioxide.
Thus vast volumes of air must be
worked over by plants in order to obtain enough carbon in the form of
carbon dioxide. In fact, if the air
were richer in this substance, plants
could grow faster and bigger than they
do now."

Hunger Signs in Crops
National Fertilizer Association, 1949

Everyone knows that plants must have fertilizer. Traditionally fertilizer has been thought of as organic matter or chemical salts which are applied directly to the soil. Not many growers think in terms of increasing the "fertilizer" content of the atmosphere in which the plants grow, despite the fact that it has been known for some time that carbon dioxide is probably the most important single chemical ingredient needed by the plant. In outdoor gardens it is impractical to think in terms of increasing the normal 300 parts per million of CO_2 in the air - how would you keep it from dispersing? In greenhouses, however, the grower can control the atmosphere. One important aspect of proper ventilation, in addition to its cooling function, is that it allows fresh carbon dioxide to enter the greenhouse, thus replacing that which the plants have consumed. One reason that greenhouse crops don't do well in the wintertime, in addition to low temperatures and an inadequate photoperiod, is that, with the vents closed to conserve heat, the CO_2 is rapidly depleted to levels far below that of the outside air.

Michael Saxton of Harvard University, the man who first informed us of this important subject, states that:

> "To some extent, extra carbon dioxide can make up for lack of light. An experiment on cucumbers shows this:

	Yield
Full sunlight.	100%
60% shade	64%
60% shade + CO_2 . .	92%
Full sunlight + CO_2 .	147%

The added carbon dioxide is almost enough to make up for the 60% shade.''

Commercial greenhouses increase the carbon dioxide levels of their structures to 1000 to 2000 parts per million. They accomplish this by several methods - liquid CO_2 or dry ice have been used, as well as the burning of a natural gas such as propane for heating. (The products of combustion from this fuel are ideally a mixture of carbon dioxide and water vapor.)

Rabbits

For our eco-system greenhouse, we have increased the CO_2 level to an estimated 700 to 800 parts per million by keeping rabbits in cages under the hydroponic tanks. An adult rabbit (the ordinary Californian or New Zealand white variety) will produce about 40 grams of carbon dioxide per day. In addition to these

Photo 11

products of respiration, the composting rabbit manure, kept in bins, provides a certain amount of CO_2 as well as nitrogen in the form of ammonia gas. This latter is also utilized by the plants, since it has been estimated that a plant can get as much as 10% of its nitrogen requirements from the air. Earthworms, which are raised in the manure bins, also produce CO_2, as well as the rich castings which are utilized as an ingredient in the organic hydroponic solution to be described later.

It is difficult for us to estimate the increase in crop yield from this technique, since we do not have another greenhouse to use as a control. Suffice it to say, subjectively, our plants this year seem larger, healthier, and bear more and bigger fruit (tomatoes) than they did last year before we added the rabbits to the eco-system. We have two color transparencies - one of the greenhouse taken in September 1974, and one taken in July 1975. The crops both seasons were the same, yet the plants photographed in July were larger and more luxuriant than those photographed two months later in the summer growing season the previous year. It is our opinion that the enrichment of the greenhouse atmosphere with "rabbit breath" made the difference.

Rabbit Management

In addition to providing an enriched carbon dioxide supply to the greenhouse, intensive rabbit culture can result in significant yields of inexpensive protein. We keep four adult rabbits in the greenhouse - one buck and three does. The gestation period of a female rabbit is a convenient thirty days - one month. Our rabbits are

bred on a rotating schedule on the first day of
every month. To illustrate: on January first,
rabbit A is bred. On February first, rabbit B
is bred, and rabbit A is giving birth to an average of seven offspring. On March first, rabbit
C is bred, rabbit B is giving birth, and rabbit
A's litter is one month old. (Rabbit A could actually be bred again at this time, but we prefer
not to work the creatures quite that much.) On
April first, rabbit A is bred again, her litter is
now two months old and ready for slaughter;
rabbit C is kindling, and rabbit B's litter is one
month old. The cycle is continued - once under-
way, on the first of the month you are always
breeding a rabbit, a litter is being born, and a
litter is ready for slaughtering. In this way, if
we assume an average of seven offspring per
kindling, each female producing four litters a
year, and all offspring harvested at a weight of

> "It is an accepted fact, proven
> by scientific experiment, that carbon
> dioxide is as necessary to the life and
> growth of a plant as oxygen is neces-
> sary to animal life. The plant needs
> a constant supply of carbon dioxide.
> This is supplied by the air which sur-
> rounds the leaves of the plant. As
> air is more or less in constant mo-
> tion a fresh supply of CO_2 is always
> available."
> Complete Book of Composting,
> Rodale, 1971

five pounds, we can ideally come up with about 420 pounds of protein per year, or 105 pounds of protein per person for a family of four. This compares favorably with the production one might attain by raising a beef cow each year, but at much less trouble and expense.

In order to get this kind of production from a herd of four rabbits, however, you must have the very best stock. Despite the mythology to the contrary, we have not found that rabbits are all that easy to raise. Some does only produce three or four in a litter, some allow their litters to die. At present, we have a buck that produces almost 100% male offspring. (The male sperm, not the female egg, determines the sex of the progeny.) This is not a problem if you are primarily interested in meat production, but it does not allow one to improve his herd by careful selection of new females. We will, of course, eventually get some new blood to upgrade the herd, but this poses something of a problem, since the nearest rabbitry with good stock is over 100 miles from us. Nevertheless, with good animals, and a program of constantly improving the herd, the above production figures could even be increased.

At present, only a comparatively small percentage of the greenhouse crops are fed to the rabbits. Often the lettuce grows faster than we can eat it, and the excess is given to them, but the bulk of their diet consists of commercial rabbit pellets. It is not possible to feed these animals, plus their numerous progeny, from the greenhouse itself - not and have much food left for ourselves! It is our intention to develop techniques for raising all of the rabbit food out-

side during the normal growing season - this
would free us from dependence upon the commercial ration. Nevertheless, the carbon dioxide
and manure they produce, not to mention their
protein, make rabbits a very important addition
to our eco-system greenhouse.

HYDROPONICS

In addition to adequate levels of light and
temperature, there are sixteen chemical ele-
ments required for the normal photosynthetic
functioning of green plants. Carbon, hydrogen
and oxygen are usually obtained from the air
and water. (It is the mixture of carbon and oxygen that makes carbon dioxide.) Of the thirteen
others, the big three, nitrogen (N), phosphorus
(P) and potassium (K) are those required in the
greatest quantity. Because of this, they are
listed among the "macronutrients," and the
percentages of N, P and K are what those three
numbers on fertilizer containers refer to. The
7-6-19 printed on a box of Hyponex, for example,
means that the chemical mixture contains seven
percent nitrogen, six percent phosphorus, and
nineteen percent potassium, or as it is sometimes also called: potash. The other macronutrients are calcium, magnesium and sulfur.
They all normally enter the plant through the
roots.

The seven "micronutrients", so called because they are required in much less concentration, are no less important to plant growth.
If the plant does not receive its needed amount
of boron, for example, it will never grow normally, and eventually die, even though the
needed amount of the nutrient may be only a few
parts per million. The same holds for the other
micronutrients which are: chlorine, copper, iron,
manganese, molybdenum and zinc.

Plants in nature obtain these essential nutrients from the soil - manure, compost, and
organic matter in general being the main source.
Microorganisms (soil bacteria) break down
these organic materials and make the nutrients
available to the plant in an inorganic form, i.e.
in the form of the chemical element concerned.
(Nitrogen is nitrogen, whether it comes from
compost or a chemical factory.) The principal
difference between chemical and organic fertilizers is essentially that the chemical fertilizer
is already in the form that the plant can use
immediately - no bacteria are needed to break
it down. Chemical fertilizers therefore act
quicker, though the essential nutrients are no
different than those released by soil bacteria
from organic sources. From the plant's point
of view, the difference between the two methods
- chemical vs. organic - is similar to the difference between medicine administered by intra-
venous injection and that given by a time-re-
lease capsule. Both medicines are identical,
the difference to the plant lies in the method of
administration and the speed at which it is able
to absorb it.

The differences to the eco-system of which the garden is a part, however, are much more profound. If chemical fertilizers are continuously administered, the soil bacteria eventually die, since there is no more organic matter for them to eat. The ultimate consequence is soil that is "dead" - nothing will grow on it unless chemical fertilizers are applied. For this reason alone, the use of chemical fertilizers is bad agriculture - despite the fact that it is now the overwhelmingly prevalent method of crop husbandry.

Chemical agriculture, along with an interlocking web of other technological "advances," has made possible an overpopulated, urbanized world. The much slower, more natural pace of the organic method does not lend itself to the speeded-up "efficiency" of mechanization. The only way that China could feed six people from one acre of land in 1907 was because probably four of them were out there continuously cultivating that acre by hand. Like the man who paints himself into a corner, the world has become so dependent upon chemical fertilizers that it is difficult to imagine any pathway back to a saner agricultural ecology short of mass starvation and all of the socio-political upheaval that goes with it. The fact that chemical fertilizers are derived largely from our rapidly dwindling supplies of petroleum only exacerbates an already dangerous situation.

For these reasons, we would never put chemical fertilizers on our soil. However, unlike some organic gardening advocates, we have no objection, per se, to plants grown with "chemicals," since all things being equal there is absolutely no difference in nutrition between vegetables grown by either method. Remember - nitrogen is nitrogen and phosphorus is phosphorus, whether it came from composted rabbit manure or a test tube. As far as the plant is concerned there can be no difference between two atoms of the same element.

Some organic gardeners exude an air of mysticism about the subject, as if there were something magic or supernatural about a phenomenon as totally natural as the sun rising and setting, or the cyclic procession of the seasons. At the same time, there is often a vehement antipathy to all things "chemical" or "scientific." (In some people's minds the two terms are almost synonymous.) Just because a perversion of science created the hydrogen bomb, ICBMs and nerve gas is no reason to repudiate the scientific frame of reference which, at its idealistic best, is nothing more than a systematic method for the understanding of nature.

Hydroponics

The vegetables in our eco-system greenhouse are raised hydroponically. Hydroponics, or soilless gardening, was originally developed as a scientific methodology to determine the nutrients essential to plant life. In order to isolate these nutrients, plants were raised without soil, receiving instead solutions of various dissolved chemical salts. By means of this technique, most of the sixteen chemical nutrients previously described were determined. From these discoveries came the era of chemical fertilizers and a distrust of "science" by a few organic extremists.

Basic to the organic method is the adage: "feed the soil, not the plant." The rationale being that with enough organic material in the soil, the plant will receive an adequate balance of nutrients. The point of view of chemical agriculture, however, is just the opposite: "feed the plant - you can't eat the soil." Obviously, when raising crops in the conventional manner in earth, the organic method is the only ecologically sane technique, for all of the reasons previously mentioned.

When raising plants in hydroponic culture, however, one must feed the plant, since the sand or gravel used as a supporting medium for the roots is completely inert, containing no nutrients at all. It is this aspect of hydroponics - the ability to feed the plant all of its essential nutrients in proper balance, in a form which makes them instantly available (plants drink their food, they can't "eat" it), and without "poisoning" anything more valuable than a few cubic feet of gravel - which makes it outproduce vegetables grown in soil three to one, or more!

In India, it has been estimated that one acre of hydroponic garden is capable of continuously supplying 1800 people with three pounds of vegetable food each day. Since we have never heard of this being done in reality, we must take such claims with a grain of salt. (Actually, we hope that the claim is the gross exaggeration it appears to be, since the last thing the world needs is the population density that such agriculture would make possible.) Suffice it to say that hydroponic gardening has the capability of providing tremendous yields of vegetable crops - much more so than is easily practical with conventional soil cultivation. It has even been suggested that the extensive use of hydroponic greenhouses, with their greater yields of produce, would actually free our cropland for organic agriculture. Even if petro-chemical nutrient solutions were applied, it would be a much better use of our dwindling petroleum supplies than burning them up in freeway commuter cars.

At this point it must be emphasized that the tremendous yields from the hydroponic method are not miracles. It is fully possible to get the same results from soil culture - the fact that the chemical makeup of hydroponic solutions is easier to control than that of soil, is what gives hydroponics its edge over other methods. There are many variables in soil culture which are not easily controlled - how much water, and when do you apply it? What is the exact chemical composition of the organic matter in the soil, and are the soil bacteria making the nutrients available in enough quantity for maximum growth? In hydroponic culture the water and the nutrients are applied at the same time, and each solution can be adjusted to meet the nutrient requirements of the specific plant under cultivation - a tremendous advantage when growing several species simultaneously in separate tanks. Plants, like animals, have differing nutritional requirements; just as a diet adequate for a sheep would starve a pig, so a balance of nutrients adequate for grapes probably wouldn't produce very many healthy tomatoes.

Generally speaking, hydroponic gardening requires that the grower know more about plant physiology and nutrient requirements than the average gardener. In a very real sense, using the hydroponic method in an eco-system greenhouse can be a consciousness-expanding activity. We call this "plant yoga."

Sub-irrigation

Most plants grown hydroponically are raised in greenhouses under carefully controlled conditions. Pea gravel is usually used as a medium for root support, and a balanced liquid mixture of all the necessary nutrients is periodically fed to the crops from below. This method is called "sub-irrigation culture." (There are other hydroponic techniques, but we will not describe them here, since sub-irrigation is by far the best method in our opinion.) In large commercial greenhouses the technique has been refined to such a degree that - once the seedlings have been planted - almost all the work is done by automation. Delicate sensors in the gravel "decide" when the plants need more solu-

Photo 12   Commercial hydroponic greenhouse

86

tion and turn on pumps which meter out the correct dosage.

Photo 13

Our System

Our eco-system set-up is much less energy-intensive. The hydroponic tanks are made from four 55-gallon drums (each cut in half lengthwise to make a total of eight containers.) At the bottom front of every trough is brazed a three-inch piece of one-half inch O. D. brass tubing. A length of ordinary garden hose (1/2" I. D.) is clamped to this tube, and the other end attached to a similar tube which has been brazed onto a five-gallon can. The insides of both the tank and the can are painted with a thick coating of an asphalt-based paint. (This is necessary to prevent the metal surfaces from rusting, since they are constantly exposed to moisture.) The tank itself is filled to within a few inches of the top with pea-sized gravel. It's essential that a small piece of galvanized or fibreglas screen be placed over the inlet tube inside the container before gravel is installed, to prevent pebbles from clogging the hose.

Planting   Our procedure for planting the tanks is to start seedlings in paper cups full of vermiculite, with the bottom of the containers perforated to allow the hydroponic solution to enter. Once the plants are well started, it's a simple matter to place the entire cup in the gravel. We have recently decided that planting the seeds directly in the gravel is probably an even better method, since sometimes the plants have trouble in getting their roots through the holes in the bottom of the cup. Peat-pots would eliminate this problem, but they eventually disintegrate into the gravel, thereby providing a medium for the growth of fungus and other undesirable microorganisms. Sowing seeds directly in the gravel is easier, though tiny seeds like carrots can get lost and usually come up in areas where you

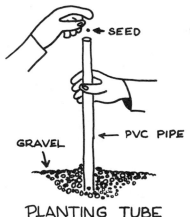

GRAVEL

PLANTING TUBE

Figure 10

didn't plant them. One way to eliminate this minor problem is to use a short length of one-half inch PVC pipe as a "planting tube." One end of the pipe is pushed into the gravel about a quarter of an inch, and the seed is dropped down the other end - thus making it easy to space your plants the way you want them.

The five-gallon can is filled with the hydroponic solution. When it's time to feed the plants, the container is lifted so that it's higher than the tank. The fluid runs down the hose and into the gravel, irrigating the plant roots from below. (That's why they call this method "sub-irrigation" culture.) As soon as the can is empty, it's placed back on the floor and the liquid flows out of the gravel, down the hose and back where it came from. In summer, we do this three times a day - morning, noon and evening - so that the roots of the crops are always moist but never actually flooded with solution for more than a few moments.

Plant nutrient requirements are ultimately related to temperature, photoperiod, and the carbon dioxide supply. If the growth rate is slow due to a deficiency in any of these factors (as in wintertime), then less nutrients are required. During the winter we feed the plants once in three days, in summer, three times in one day. As you advance in your plant yoga, you'll know instinctively when they require feeding.

An Automated System

Lifting a five-gallon can full of 40 pounds of nutrient solution three times a day may not be everyone's idea of pleasant exercise. The system could easily be automated with very little trouble and minimal drain on the wind-electric

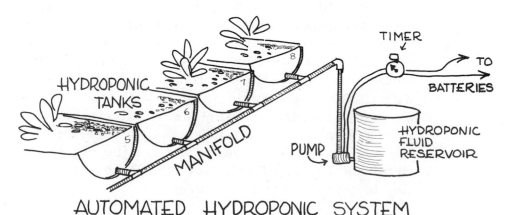

AUTOMATED HYDROPONIC SYSTEM

Figure 11

system. A large drum provided with a small pump could be connected to the hydroponic tanks by a manifold. A simple timer switch could be activated every four hours (or any convenient interval, depending upon conditions) to pump the nutrients from the drum to the gravel beds. When the drum was empty, the pump would shut off, and the liquid then run by gravity back into storage. For this to work, of course, the lowest part of the gravel tanks would have to be above the level of the full drum.

There is no reason at all why the gravel-filled 55-gallon drum halves couldn't be replaced by other plant growing containers. A wooden box, caulked at the seams and painted with asphalt paint would make an even better tank than the steel drum halves, since no matter what you paint the latter with, they eventually rust.

Taste of Hydroponic Vegetables

One sometimes hears the complaint that hydroponic vegetables (usually tomatoes) bought in supermarkets taste bland and pulpy. The explanation for this (aside from the fact that supermarket produce is of dubious freshness) is that tomatoes grown in commercial hydroponic greenhouses are special hybrids, bred for color, uniformity in size, and the ability to all ripen at the same time - qualities which have nothing to do with flavor, but everything to do with the convenience and profit of the agribusinessman who raises them. No special hybrids for us - the tomatoes we raise in our tanks are the same varieties we raise in the garden - Burpee Big Boy being our particular favorite.

To test for ourselves if hydroponic produce
has a different flavor, last summer Elizabeth
took two tomatoes - one from the garden and one
from a hydroponic tank in the greenhouse; she
sliced them and placed each on a
separate plate - no one else
knew which was which.
None of the family could
detect any differences in
flavor, nor could we guess
which tomato came from
the tank, and which
from the garden.

**Organic
Hydroponics**

About the only criticism of hydroponic gardening that we will accept as valid is that it re-
lies (for the most part) on chemicals which are
derived from fossil fuels, or which use vast
amounts of fossil fuels in their manufacture.
For that reason we have been working with various organic hydroponic solutions, and have been
both surprised and delighted with the results of
our very first efforts.

Since the hydroponic method was originally
developed as a scientific means of determining
the mineral nutrients required by plants, it is
not surprising that in its commercial applications it has traditionally relied on pure chemical salts for its solutions. Very little research
seems to have been done with organically derived formulas. Perhaps the most notable work
was carried out in India. J. S. Douglas, in his
book Hydroponics - The Bengal System, describes

the use of perforated earthenware vessels which are sunk into the gravel beds and kept filled with various types of manure or composted organic materials. Water is flushed through the gravel in the usual manner for nutrient solutions, and the contents of the compost pots are then slowly leached into the aggregate and made available to the plant roots.

Fish Tank Nutrient Solution

Another experiment with an organic nutrient solution is briefly described on page 135 of Energy Primer (Portola Institute, 1974). This method uses the water from aquaculture tanks as a growth medium:

> "Finally, associated with each main (fish) tank is a hydroponic growing compartment where the culture water from the main tanks (a 'soup' of excellent fertilizer) is flushed through gravel beds planted with vegetable crops."

Our initial feeling when we read this was that the fish tank water would probably not provide an adequate "diet" of nutrients for optimum growth. Consequently, to test this, we started some hydroponic pinto beans, using only the water from the aquaculture tank as a culture medium. At first, these plants put on amazing growth - rising several inches above their contemporaries growing in a commercial solution. Then, after a couple of weeks, the "commercial" beans began to catch up with those receiving only fish tank water. By the end of the month, the fish tank beans had all but stopped growing and were pale and sickly in appearance, while the other beans were in all respects normal.

Photo 14   Bean plants raised in three different solutions

These results seem to be confirmed by an experiment conducted at the U.S. Fish & Wildlife Service's fish farming experiment station in Stuttgart, Arkansas. In the May/June 1975 issue of Aquaculture and the Fish Farmer, Sneed, Allen and Ellis report on the experiment, which involved flushing the effluent from a raceway complex containing 10,000 pounds of channel catfish into hydroponic troughs containing 17 varieties of vegetables. In general, the results of the experiment were disappointing:

"The yield of edible tissue varied widely among different vegetable varieties. Although (all) varieties produced some edible tissue, eleven were of very poor quality and quantity. Three varieties produced average yields and three produced yields considered to be above

average for home gardens. The best
yields were produced by green peas
and cucumbers. "

In most cases, then, people who are com-
bining aquaculture with hydroponics should consider using the fish tank water as an excellent
"starter" - a basic solution with which to mix
other organic materials.

Lawrence D. Weiss, in the May 14, 1973
issue of The Tribal Messenger, gives us a clue
as to how to mix an organic hydroponic solution:

"Once the location of the hydroponic
installation has been determined, and the
troughs built, the hard work is done with.
The last major concern is the nutrient
solution itself. Home-made mixtures of
such things as well-rotted compost and
animal manure are cheap and ecological.
The home farmer can experiment with
different such nutrients and strengths
in the water base. In this way he or
she will find the combination most suitable for his or her plants and installation. "

Using both fish tank and well water as our
base, we mixed several different strengths,
mixes and types of organic material - in effect,
making what is familiar to most organic gardeners as "manure tea." We used these solutions
on tomatoes, radishes, lettuce, runner and pinto
beans. (Most of the initial experiments were
with beans.) At the same time, identical plants
received the commercial hydroponic solution
(Hyponex: 7-6-19).

At first, we were very "scientific" - carefully weighing out 20 grams of rabbit manure
per liter of water, for example. We soon realized
that such careful measurements weren't necessary, and that in any case most Americans
wouldn't bother with them. (It's hard enough to
persuade people to try a new gardening technique
without throwing the metric system at them!)
At any rate, in our experience it didn't seem to
matter - we wound up by mixing a standard
formula of:

    one part rabbit manure
    one part chicken manure
    one part earthworm castings (manure)
    one part wood ashes (rich in
                  potassium)

The measure used was a small Quaker Oats
box, filled to the top. The only convenient container we had for mixing these ingredients was
a 20-gallon can, which was filled within an inch
or so of the top with either well or fish tank
water. (We can't honestly say we noticed any
difference between the two, though it stands to
reason that the fish tank liquid would have more
nutrients in it.) Rain water should not be used,
however, since it is probably deficient in the
micro-nutrients (manganese, boron, etc.) which
are usually always present as impurities in
ground water.

The organic ingredients were vigorously
stirred into the water and then allowed to steep
for several days, by which time all solid particles had settled to the bottom. The liquid (the
color of a weak cup of tea) was then carefully

poured off into cans and fresh water added to the container for a new batch. We found that we could get several batches of hydroponic fluid from one batch of organic material. From time to time we would add fresh measures of the organic mix to the liquid - relying, mostly, we must admit, on when it felt right to do so. (Plant yoga again!)

Testing the pH

At first, we very religiously tested the pH of the solutions. pH is the measure of how acid or alkaline a material is. (Plants will only thrive within certain rather narrow pH ranges.) All of the books on hydroponics really stress the importance of this, but in our experience, the pH of our solutions, both organic and commercial, has always been right about where it should be - between 6.0 and 7.0. The pH test is made with a special indicator paper called Nitrazine paper, available in most any drug store. When a strip of paper is dipped in the fluid to be tested it will change color depending on the pH - yellow for strongly acid, blue for strongly alkaline, with several ranges in between. The color of the paper is matched against a color chart on the side of the container it comes in. (For people who are unfamiliar with this very simple test, don't be alarmed - it isn't any big deal.) If the solution turns out to be too alkaline, an acid must be added to bring it in line with the proper pH, or if too acid, an alkali or base must be added. Commercial hydroponic greenhouses use, of course, pure hydrochloric acid or sodium hydroxide to balance the pH of their nutrient solutions. Since both of these chemicals are extremely dangerous, as well as expensive, we have relied on white vinegar (acid) or baking soda (alkali-base) with no problems at all. To someone who has no familiarity with simple chemistry, this may sound horribly complex - it isn't, and no one should be scared off from trying hydroponics because of it. Actually, we have seldom ever had to adjust the pH of our solutions - to the point that we practically never even test them anymore.

First Test Results

The results of our experiments indicate that almost any organically-derived solution will grow plants. The bean plants raised in a pure chicken manure solution grew just as well as those raised with the above described mixture. We must also be honest and state that two "control" plants, raised in pure worm castings (no soil at all) grew just as well as any of the hydroponic plants, including those receiving the commercial solution. (This may provide an alternative for those who object to the hydroponic concept.) In general, the commercial solution plants grew slightly faster than the organic solution plants, but not significantly so. The most striking difference between the two solutions was that the organic plants did not wilt during the hottest part of the day, while the plants raised with the commercial solution almost always wilted! We observed this phenomenon take place every day, so it isn't a figment of our imagination.

An excessively high nutrient salt concentration near the plant roots can cause the plant to lose water to the soil, or in our case, to the gravel. The result is wilting of the leaves. Since the commercial solution plants were probably receiving a higher concentration of nutrients than the organic solution plants, this provides an explanation for the wilting phenomenon. Bear in mind that the summer greenhouse temperatures, even with all vents open, sometimes go as high as 104° F. - a temperature at which any self-respecting plant would wilt! Within five minutes of being fed the nutrient solution, however, all symptoms disappeared - the same as when you water wilting plants in the garden or in pots.

We do not feel that we have even begun to develop a perfect organic hydroponic solution, but are well pleased with the results of our first experiments. Since our tests were quite modest, we hesitate to make definitive statements. We did note, however, that the organic solution plants, in addition to their wilt resistance, seemed to both flower and produce ripe fruit sooner than the plants grown with the commercial solution.

Much work remains to be done. For those
readers interested in experimenting with organic
hydroponic solutions, The Complete Book of
Composting, (Rodale Books, Inc., 1971), lists the
nitrogen, phosphorus and potassium percentages
of most common organic materials. (For example,
rabbit manure has NPK percentages of 7.0, 2.4,
and 0.6). By composting appropriate mixtures
of organic materials, then leaching them with
water, hydroponic solutions of varying NPK percentages can be produced.

Apparently the other nutrients - both macro-
and micro - are usually present in sufficient
quantities in the water or organic material to
produce adequate growth. Using our organic
fluids we have never experienced any plant deficiency symptoms attributable to minerals
other than nitrogen. (The beans grown in the
pure fish tank water were deficient in this element.)

As far as we are able to determine, organic
hydroponics is a wide open field. Needless to
say, if an organic solution capable of consistent
results is developed, the implications for future
world agriculture could be significant.

GREENHOUSE MANAGEMENT

We have seen how the optimum photosynthetic functioning of green plants is dependent
upon complex interrelationships of temperature,
light, and carbon dioxide supply, and how the
plant roots and stem act as a water system
which transports the proper mixture of dissolved
mineral nutrients to where they can complete
their part of the process. If we are sensitive to
the harmony of these interactions we will have
constructed our greenhouse to provide for their
fulfillment. As eco-system gardeners, we are a
necessary link in this chain of relationships,
for it is our management which keeps the process in motion. While we are providing for the
plants, the plants are providing for us - in more
ways than one, since the permanent alteration
of the operator's consciousness engendered by
working with such a system is probably equally
as important as the food it produces. If everyone had an eco-system greenhouse, we doubt
there would be an environmental crisis in the

world today: It is one thing to read about ecological laws - it is quite another to experience their full reality in your everyday life. If we accept the notion that the goal of all true religion is to unite the individual spirit with the whole reality of which it is a part, then the laws of ecology might fit that definition better than some, and an eco-system greenhouse, properly apprehended, might fulfill the role of a church better than many.

Sowing & Reaping

Proper management of the eco-system is the key to maximum productivity. Like anything else, you reap pretty much what you sow, and if you want continuous reaping you must be prepared for continuous sowing. It is as simple as that, and it is surprising how long it took us to discover a fact so obvious. Rule number one is: never allow a productive square inch to remain fallow. Even if only a radish or two, always plant seeds just as soon as space is available for them. This will involve some judgements on your part, and often mean the ruthless termination of plants that have passed their prime in order to make room for new growth.

Effective Growing Season Again

For example, in the fall of 1974 we kept some tomatoes from the summer crop alive until past Thanksgiving - despite the fact that their maximum fruit production, which reached its peak in August, had long since passed. For the sake of a few pale and sickly tomatoes, we sacrificed valuable growing space which would have been better utilized for an autumn crop of peas, lettuce, spinach and cabbage. A few entries from our 1974 greenhouse journal give the picture:

10/23/74 - Took out squash plant in #2 - it was about done and had aphids crawling all over it.

10/30/74 - Cold, windy and damp weather for last 2 days - am now feeding the plants only twice a day - a.m. and p.m. Plants are not doing much these days - it's probably about over for them as far as much growth is concerned. Explore idea of waning photoperiod in addition to cold temperature as factor in plant decline. (Anything planted in autumn is "doomed"?)

11/6/74 - Everything slowed down almost to standstill. Tomatoes take weeks to ripen, and then never seem to get much beyond a pale salmon color. Cukes grow very, very slowly. Even so-called cool weather crops are not growing - lettuce, spinach and Chinese cabbage seedlings are still seedlings after almost a month. (Planted 10/18).

11/21/74 - Took out tomato plant in tank #2 - yellowing, mottled leaves, and weird warts on main stem. Rough fruit which was splitting. General vibes of plant were very sick. One new sprout from main stem near roots looked very healthy, so I left it to form new plant.

11/22/74 - Took out tomato plant in rear of tank #7 - no more fruit. Also, it small and puny. Never was much of a plant.

11/23/74 - Took out tomato in #3 - similar reasons as above. Liz transplanted one head lettuce from #7 to #2 and endive from #3 to #2. Root systems on both plants have not yet broken through paper cups. These were planted as seedlings 10/18 - not much growth. Cleaned up greenhouse a bit - pruned tomatoes in #7 & #8. Changed hydroponic chemicals.

11/27/74 - Greenhouse thermometer shows 32° F. this a.m. - plants not frozen, but they don't look very happy. Tomato in #7 is getting yellowed leaves.

11/28/74 - Thanksgiving Day - Got down to 32° again last nite. Cuke plant looks as if some of the leaves froze. Lettuce plants (planted 10/18) are now 3" - 5" high. Still just seedlings. Spinach plants same date only 2-1/2" high. Tomatoes look as if they're dying of old age. All the algae in the fish tank seems dead and gone.

11/30/74 - Freeze out - 27° F. last night. Everything seems done in, though lettuce and spinach might pull through. P.M. - pulled all plants, except seedlings in #2, 4 & 5.

1/4/75 - Pulled last of lettuce, frozen solid.

These notes confirm the information found in Figure 3, as well as suggest some improved management techniques. Let's take each pertinent entry and, with the gift of hindsight, analyze what we did wrong.

Cool & Warm Season Crops

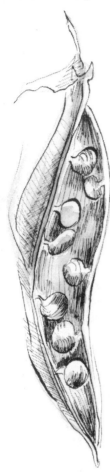

To begin with, the October 23rd entry was made 2 days past the end of the effective growing season as shown in Fig. 3. The fact that we pulled a warm season plant like squash so late in the cycle, indicates that we'd not yet learned to manage our greenhouse efficiently. Any plant should be terminated just as soon as it passes its peak in productivity - for warm season plants like tomatoes, squash and cucumbers, this would be sometime in August in our part of the country. As soon as the tanks are free, cool season crops like lettuce, carrots, spinach, peas and cabbage should be planted. This gives the new seedlings a chance to get off to a good start before the coming colder weather and shorter days have a chance to slow them down. We have found that seedlings which do not put on rapid growth their first few weeks never amount to much as plants. Don't waste your time trying to nurse recalcitrant seedlings into health - it's best to pull them and start over with fresh stock. Again, your increasing experience with the system will eventually tell you when this is advisable.

The fact that the squash plant referred to in the October 23rd entry was infested with aphids also indicates that it was past its prime. We have found that insects do not tend to infest healthy young plants. If a plant is infested with insects, it is either old, unhealthy, or most likely, both. We are not speaking here of a few aphids crawling on a few leaves, but of actual infestations of many hundreds of insects.

Insects can become a serious problem in
greenhouses, and we have no easy solutions.
When aphids seemed to be getting the upper
hand, and the plants infected still had a few
weeks of productivity left, we released a half-
pint of ladybugs in the greenhouse. (Available
by mail from many sources - see the ads in the
back of Organic Gardening & Farming magazine.)
For several days it was difficult to work inside
without stepping on them, since they swarmed
everywhere. Within a week, however, they had
destroyed virtually every aphid and, since there
was then nothing left for them to eat, they exited
via the open ventilators. This method of pest
control is certainly more aesthetic than the application of pesticides, though it isn't a solution
for all insect problems. White fly is a perennial
greenhouse pest, and ladybugs won't eat them.
Since they seem to have no natural enemies,
poison sprays appear to be the only answer.

It is at this point that the mettle of any organic gardener is really tested. It's one thing
to give lip service to anti-pesticide sentiments,
it's quite another to see your greenhouse being
taken over by millions of white flies. Rotenone,
a so-called "safe" pesticide, was totally ineffec-
tive, as was Malathion, a not-so-safe insect
killer. The only way we've been able to get rid
of white flies is to ruthlessly pull all of the plants
infested with them. Since these are almost always old plants, the loss isn't as great as it
might appear to be. If white fly is detected early
enough - before there are too many of them -
spraying plain water on the leaves is usually
effective. Spraying plants with water in a greenhouse on occasion is a good practice anyway.

Feeding Schedule

In the entry for October 30th, it is noted that the plants are now only fed twice a day. Actually, the three-times-a-day schedule could have been terminated a month earlier. Multiple feedings are necessary only during the hot days of summer to prevent wilting, but in cooler periods of the year there is no need for it. In spring and autumn we feed the plants in the morning when we get up, and again around 3:00 p.m. This varies according to weather conditions: on unusually hot days, three feedings may be in order, whereas on cold, cloudy days one may be all that is necessary. Many references on hydroponic gardening state that only one feeding per day is required. Since our experience has been otherwise, particularly in the summer, we can only suggest that each person do what seems best for his specific conditions. Suffice it to say that when the plants begin to droop and wilt, feeding is in order.

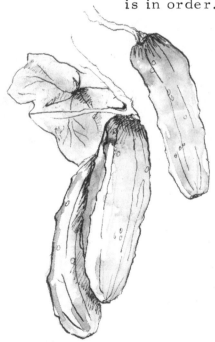

The entry for November 6th confirms what we said earlier - warm weather plants like tomatoes and cucumbers require minimum temperatures of 60° F. for optimum growth. A glance at Fig. 4 tells us that the greenhouse low average temperature for the month of Scorpio, 1974, was only 41 degrees - nineteen degrees colder than the minimum. The fact that the lettuce, spinach and Chinese cabbage seedlings mentioned here are not growing well can be attributed to the fact that they were planted only three days before the October 21st cut-off date.

The remaining entries give the details of what you can expect during the winter "growing season" with an unheated greenhouse and no photoperiod supplement. If you are content with an eight month greenhouse, then October 21st is the end of your gardening, and you must wait until the 21st of February before any practical plant growth can again be expected. We have outlined how adequate temperature control and artificial lighting can overcome these handicaps, but the added expense for such measures must be weighed against their advantages.

There is just no substitute for experience in hydroponic greenhouse gardening, and since we have found that our experience sometimes contradicts the information found in the literature on the subject, so you may find that some of our techniques won't work under your specific conditions. We have learned not to worry about this phenomenon - the world is full of "experts" who contradict each other, and while it is valuable to read everything you can about a subject, the "expert's" information is only as useful as its applicability to your own experience. Never be afraid to experiment, and don't worry too much if your definition of reality doesn't jibe exactly with someone else's - it's a phenomenon basic to the human condition.

Since finances have not yet allowed us to carry on winter growth experiments under artificial lights, we will discuss our experience with the greenhouse as an eight month growing structure. The following planting schedules should be considered as points of departure only; unless your environmental conditions are quite similar to ours, we would expect that adjustments to your local eco-system will be necessary.

**Experience
is the
Best Teacher**

The Spring Crop

We have discovered that February 21st is an almost magical day; for two consecutive years now, it has been the date when plant growth again becomes noticeable after four months of dormancy. The seeds of cool weather crops may now be planted in the gravel tanks, or, if you wish to get an even bigger jump on the season, they may be started earlier in the house in paper cups full of vermiculite for transplanting around the the 21st as seedlings.

Since the weather is still quite cold, your greenhouse will have to be heated, or at least well insulated. We've already discussed many methods of accomplishing this. One idea that we have not yet tried is to use dark colored, even black, gravel as our root-support medium in the hydroponic tanks. Aggregate of any kind makes an excellent solar heat storage "battery," and since dark pigments absorb heat much more efficiently than light pigments, a black gravel would provide our seedlings with extra warmth around the roots. We have found that the ordinary light grey pea gravel will hold temperatures well above the freezing point, even with night time air temperatures dropping into the low twenties. Black gravel should do even better, although such material would probably be entirely too hot for the summer growing season. The leveled gravel on the surface of each tank could be sprayed with black paint before the

seeds or seedlings were planted. Then, later
in the cycle when temperatures get too hot, it
could easily be raked over to change the dark
surface back to a light one.

The cool weather vegetables which we plant
in the spring and autumn are:

1. Lettuce (loose-leaf) - 40 days
2. Carrots - 65 days
3. Spinach - 42 days
4. Swiss chard - 60 days
5. Radish - 22 days
6. Chinese cabbage - 70 days
7. Peas - 55 days
8. Onions - 100 days (not planted for
        autumn crop, since onions
        require a long photoperiod
        for full development of
        bulbs.)
8. Turnips (for greens) - 45 days

The following chart shows how these spring
crops might be planted in our eight hydroponic
tanks:

Figure 12

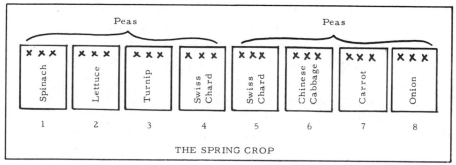

Peas are planted at the rear of each tank where they can climb on pieces of chicken wire placed against the north wall for that purpose. Always place the tallest growing plants in the rear, since then they cannot block the sunlight from the shorter vegetables. Until the peas grow tall enough to cover them, aluminum foil reflectors should be placed against the wall to increase the light intensity. Ours are simply 16-inch squares of 1/4 inch plywood covered with heavy-duty kitchen foil. They should be angled enough to reflect the maximum amount of light on the plants.

Radishes, the fastest growing vegetables we raise, are inter-cropped among all of the other varieties in every tank. As soon as they mature, they are harvested, and other seeds are sown. We are continually looking for space to plant radishes, and keep a packet of seeds within reach at all times.

Transition to Warm Season Crop

Spinach, lettuce, Swiss chard and Chinese cabbage can all be trimmed as their outer leaves become large enough to eat, thus allowing more than one meal from the same plants. As the season progresses, however, you will want to begin making room for your warm season crops. If all of the above vegetables were planted around the 21st of February, you should begin eating spinach, lettuce and turnip greens about the first of April, with Swiss chard and peas coming two weeks later. The first of May is not too soon to begin planting tomato seedlings (we don't recommend planting tomato seeds directly in the tank.) Your peas should still be producing at this time, however, so you'll have to decide if you want to pull them to make room for the tomatoes. (Since tomatoes are tall plants, they should always be placed, like the peas, against the north wall.) If your peas are still producing a lot, the tomatoes can wait for a couple of weeks, though they should be in by the 15th of May. At the risk of being tedious, we must repeat that these data reflect our own particular conditions. Generally speaking, when the inside average low temperatures get near fifty degrees, the time to plant warm season crops has arrived.

Our usual warm season crops are:

1. Tomatoes - 70 days
2. Peppers - 70 days
3. Snap beans - 50 days
4. Cucumber - 70 days
5. Squash - 60 days

These are planted in addition to enough lettuce plants to keep us in summer salads and, of course, enough radishes to fill up any odd spaces not already covered. Readers familiar with the French Intensive method of organic gardening may recognize our rationale for planting the hydroponic beds, which is essentially: make every square inch of growing space productive. The Postage Stamp Garden Book - how to grow all the food you can eat in very little space, by Duane Newcomb, is an excellent reference for this method of intensive planting.

Pollination

Most warm season vegetables are raised or their fruits rather than their foliage. This means that their flowers must be pollinated, and since the greenhouse is a more or less closed environment, the wind and insects which usually perform this vital function cannot be relied upon. Hand pollination is in order - a simple task which can be carried out during the time the plants are being fed each morning.

For squash plants, with their large flowers, a chicken feather makes an adequate pollinator: pollen from the male flowers is gathered on the tip of the feather and transferred to the female flowers. The way to tell the difference between the two is that the female blossom sprouts from the end of a tiny squash, whereas the male looks like an ordinary flower. The same holds for cucumber blossoms - the first time you see the difference, you'll never mistake them. Sometimes male flowers will be open when there are no females ready, and vice-versa. For this reason, it is helpful to have more than one squash plant, since the chances of both male and female flowers being open simultaneously are increased. The drawback to this, of course, is that squash plants are very large, and take up an inordinate amount of greenhouse space. We usually pull our squash plants when those in the outside garden begin producing, thus making room in the tanks for less bulky vegetables.

Tomatoes produce many more and much smaller flowers than squash, so the chicken feather technique isn't practical. The best method of pollination is to just flick each flower lightly with your finger. If you hold a piece of

black paper behind the flower as you do this,
you'll be able to see the pollen as it is released.

We think that the key to raising greenhouse
tomatoes efficiently lies in pinching off each
plant's growing tip just as soon as the fifth truss
has formed. The so-called "truss" is the little
branch which holds the flowers, and ultimately,
of course, the tomatoes themselves. Five trusses
of tomatoes are about all one plant can efficiently
produce within the space of the warm season
growing period, and any further fruit set only

Photo 15   Tomatoes growing in gravel

takes energy away from them. Experienced tomato growers, of course, already know that the
"suckers" which appear just between the main
stem and the side branches should be removed
as soon as they appear. If not, the plant becomes
bushy with too much of its energy going into the
production of useless foliage. Wittwer and Honma suggest that the circulation of air and carbon

dioxide can be improved by regularly pruning
the tomato leaves up to the level of the ripening
fruit. This practice makes good sense, and certainly results in a neater looking greenhouse. It
also leaves fewer hiding places for white flies
and other insect pests.

Cucumbers usually produce many, many
more male than female blossoms, and while they
can be pollinated by hand, we have found that they
manage to pollinate themselves without any help.
Perhaps the occasional breezes coming in the
open vents are enough to do the trick. Unless
you have an inordinate appetite for cucumbers,
you'll find that one vine is more than enough to
provide all you can eat in salads, plus a good
surplus for making pickles. In addition, a cuke
vine can dominate a tremendous amount of space

Photo 16   June 27, 1975 – cucumber taking over far wall

in a small greenhouse. We never cease to marvel at the yearly cucumber jungle created by only one plant. Next year we intend to train the vine outside via a ventilator opening, so that it won't shade such a large growing area. The same technique could be used for melons, since at our altitude they are impossible to raise in the outside garden, and are much too large a plant to grow in the greenhouse.

Reasonably heavy string, stretched from the greenhouse rafters, is necessary to provide an adequate climbing support for your beans and cucumber vines. Try to run the string in such a way that the lush growth of these plants won't shade the other crops too much. A little shading in a summer greenhouse can help to keep the temperatures from getting too hot, but too much shade will cut the growth of other plants. When we pulled a large squash plant in mid-summer, Elizabeth planted a morning glory vine in the vacated tank to provide a little color; it never grew enough to produce one flower because the cucumber jungle in that part of the greenhouse blocked almost all of the sunlight.

Transition to Fall Crop

By the 21st of August, most of the warm season crops will have passed their peak of productivity. This is the time to harden your heart and start pulling every plant that is past its prime in order to make room for the fall crop of cool weather vegetables. These, with the exception of onions, will be the same as your spring crop.

Hi-Lo Thermometer

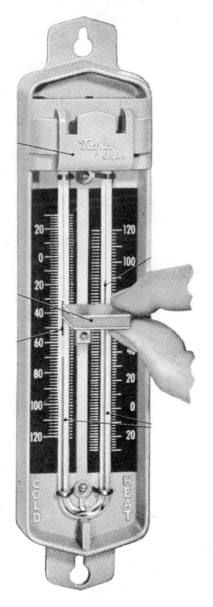

Essential to any greenhouse is a high/low thermometer. This is an ingenious device which will record the highest and lowest temperatures during a given period. It is also helpful to have an identical thermometer outside the greenhouse. In this way, you can keep records of the daily high and low temperatures, inside and outside, throughout the yearly cycle. After you've done this for a year, you'll begin to understand your local eco-system much better, and be able to intelligently plan your planting dates. After two years of making these records, a non-verbal intuition begins to form in your consciousness, and you'll understand how so-called peasant and primitive farmers "know" when the optimum time has come to plant, cultivate, and harvest. There is no magic in this - it is just being in tune with your environment. We have even progressed to the point where we can accurately estimate the number of amperes being generated

by our wind-electric system, just by feeling the
wind on our faces and observing how the trees
bend. Technology need not estrange us from
nature - it can put us in tune with it.

Hydroponic Chemicals

A hydroponic greenhouse, of course, requires
some different maintenance routines than a conventional forcing structure. Since the technique
uses the same solution over and over again, it is
well adapted to arid climates - in Africa's Kala-
hari Desert, for example, an outdoor hydroponic
facility uses only one-twentieth the amount of
water required by conventional agriculture.
Even so, the hydroponic solutions must be
changed periodically, although we've found that
this need not be done quite as often as some of
the literature recommends. The commercial
chemical mixture that we started out with was
Hyponex - available in powder form from most
nurseries. The manufacturer recommends
changing chemicals weekly, although we've found
that they can be used with no apparent ill effect
on the plants for two weeks and longer. Even if
you intend to use an organic hydroponic solution,
we recommend that you start with a commercial
chemical mixture to familiarize yourself with
the technique. Once you understand how it all
works, you can begin trying organic experiments.
The plants grown in a correctly prepared commercial solution will give you a standard of com-
parison for the organic mix, so that when your
organic plants equal or outgrow the chemical
ones, you'll know you've won the game.

Test Kit   If you're really scientifically oriented, you might want to purchase a hydroponic solutions testing kit. This is essentially a specialized chemistry set designed for use by commercial hydroponic greenhouses. It will tell you the exact chemical breakdown in parts per million of any nutrient solution - a tremendous advantage when trying to formulate an adequate organic mixture.

We purchased the La Motte Plant Nutrition Kit, Model AM-41 (Code 5406), available from the La Motte Chemical Products Company, Chestertown, Maryland 21620. The kit is not cheap - ours cost over $100. - but it can save a lot of blind experimenting. Actually, since we aren't the chemistry-set types, we haven't used the kit as much as we should, instead relying on the Complete Book of Composting (Rodale), for its average chemical analyses of various organic materials. We don't necessarily recommend this method over the test kit - it just reflects our personal bewilderment with using vials, flasks, pipettes and parts per million measurements.

In thinking about this section, we have again glanced through our literature about hydroponics; much of it, slanted toward the large commercial growers, almost requires a degree in chemistry to understand. We have not found the hydroponic method to be at all complicated or difficult, though in writing a book about it we are aware that conditions in other parts of the country might be different enough from ours to cause problems. For example, we use our own well

118

water as the base of our solutions, and have
never yet had any difficulties with pH or unwanted
chemical content. Many of the references recommend that the grower have his water ana-
lyzed - since the micro-nutrients often exist as
impurities in the local water supply, it is a good
idea to know where you are before you begin.
Also, just because we've had no problems with
pH doesn't mean that you won't. Since all of the
references stress the importance of regular pH
tests, we can only assume that we are fortunate
in seldom ever having to make these adjustments
in our hydroponic solutions. (Not that it is at all
difficult.)

Users of city water supplies might find it
necessary to allow their water to sit in an open
drum for a few days to allow the chlorine to dis-
sipate. Also, the gravel beds should be flushed
periodically with plain water to remove any
build-up of impurities - we do this just before
planting each new crop. In the summer, when the
plants are transpiring a lot, be prepared to top
off each solution container every day with water.
It is amazing how much water a plant can use up
in a 24-hour period - our fast growing cucumber
used more than a gallon a day last July!

Animal Feed

One technique you may wish to try is to
raise hydroponic oats, barley, or rye grass as
animal feed during the cool season. We covered
the bottom of some shallow trays with a layer of
rye seed, and using a similar technique as you
would for growing sprouts for your own use,
flushed the seeds daily with hydroponic solution.
The result within a week or so was a tightly
woven mat of sprouted grass - an excellent fresh
green feed for rabbits or goats in the winter.

In concluding this chapter we can only say again that we are totally sold on hydroponics - despite the chemical mumbo-jumbo found in some of the literature, we have never raised so many vegetables so quickly with so little trouble. Try it and see if you don't agree.

Photo 17   Fourteen pints of pickles
– partial harvest from one vine

ACCESS

Hydroponic Chemicals

1. Hyponex
        Hydroponic Chemical Co.
        Copley, Ohio 44321

2. Continental Nutriculture Co.
        Box 6751, Lubbock, Texas 79409
        (manufacture a custom formula based on
        chemical content of local water supply
        and individual growing conditions.)

3. Super-Gro
        Hydroponics Co.
        P.O. Box 3215, Little Rock, Ark. 72201

AQUACULTURE

Aquaculture is the intensive cultivation of
fish or other cold-blooded aquatic animals such
as mussels, clams and crayfish under optimum
growing conditions. Fish farming - perhaps a
more descriptive term - has been practiced for
thousands of years in the Orient, and has recently
become a profitable business in the United States.
Catfish are raised on large farms throughout the
South, and in Louisiana crayfish culture has
proven to be a profitable commercial venture.
In mountainous states such as Idaho, where an
abundance of cold running water is available,
fish farms provide the market with pan-sized
rainbow trout at premium prices.

In this country, aquaculture - like most other
farming - is run along agribusiness lines, with
an eye toward maximum yields and maximum
profits. Fish are "packed like sardines" in ponds
or tanks in which the water is constantly circulated, filtered and aerated to keep the inhabitants
from dying in their own waste products. These
fish feedlots make use of high-protein "chows"

manufactured by the major livestock ration companies, and hence bear no relationship at all to
the organic low-energy aquaculture operations
of the Orient ... which, interestingly enough,
consistently out-produce the "agribiz" methods
normally used in America.

Advantages

We became interested in organic aquaculture
in 1971 after reading a series of articles on the
subject by Dr. John Todd and Dr. William Mc-
Larney in Organic Gardening and Farming magazine. These two researchers, working at the
New Alchemy Institute in Woods Hole, Massachusetts, have been experimenting for many years
with low-energy organic food-producing methods
designed for homesteads and small communities.
In an article entitled "Aquaculture on the Organic
Farm and Homestead," appearing in the August
1971 issue of OGF, Dr. McLarney summed up
the rationale behind fish farming:

> "The best argument for aquaculture
> is based on the ever-increasing need
> for protein foods. Fishes and aquatic
> invertebrates are far more efficient
> food converters than their warm-blooded
> counterparts, since they need expend
> little or no energy supporting their
> weight or maintaining their body tem-
> peratures. They are thus capable of
> producing more protein per unit area
> from the same amount of food."

Compare Robert Rodale's comment on the
food-converting efficiency of warm-blooded animals (OGF, April 1971):

"Warm-blooded land animals are
monstrously inefficient producers of
nutritious food, and their meat will
become more and more of a luxury as
the population increases and good agricultural land becomes more scarce.
Almost 90 percent of the food given to
beef cattle, for example, is "wasted"
because it is used to keep up the animal's body temperature. The harvest
of protein food in the form of meat is
small in return for the corn, grain and
hay that is invested in supporting the
animals. "

The weight-gaining efficiency of cold-blooded
aquatic animals, plus the heat-retaining properties of water make aquaculture a very attractive
component of an eco-system greenhouse, since
the water mass used to buffer winter temperatures is also utilized for another protein crop.
Every inch of precious greenhouse space is
thereby used to maximum advantage.

Unfortunately, our initial aquaculture experiments have proven to be dismal failures - another
example of plausible concepts being demolished
by thermodynamic realities. We are not saying,
however, that aquaculture cannot be made to
work in a system like ours, just that we were
very naive in our original approach. Fish, like
all living things, must be provided with a full
range of specific requirements if they are to
measure up to an optimum standard of growth,
and these requirements, like everything else in
the eco-system, are a complex tangle of interrelationships.

Each organism in nature is adapted to a specific environment, and one could legitimately say that since each is necessary to the other, they constitute one reality. Just as a frog minus its environment is no longer an integral whole, the environment minus its frog is also incomplete. In nature, this "environmental organism" continually exchanges energy within its parts - plants feed animals and animals feed plants - constituting a continuous dance of solar energy in its myriad manifestations.

When attempting to create an artificial "environmental organism" such as our eco-system, we must pay constant attention to all of its interactions to insure that one part doesn't unbalance the whole. With greenhouse vegetables this is not much of a problem. However, because they are adapted to an aquatic world which is "alien" to our terrestrial frame of reference, fish have many life requirements which are not immediately obvious.

Requirements of Aquatic Life

The first thing any organism needs is space to live. In nature a given body of water will support an optimum number of fish; such an environment would be said to be in balance when the food, oxygen supply and water temperature were all at an adequate level to support this optimum population. All four factors: space, temperature, food and oxygen, are interrelated with the fifth factor of population density.

The most obvious difference between an intensive aquaculture operation and a natural environment is that nature never allows the population densities possible in a managed system.

To this extent, our eco-system really isn't an "eco-system" at all, since we are eliminating all possible factors which would prohibit maximum production of selected plant and animal species. We are the only predators in our eco-system, and we see to it that every condition is met for the highest yields attainable. While each carp living in a natural body of water might have thousands of gallons of water at its disposal, that same fish in an intensive aquaculture system might have only one gallon or less!

The Max Planck Institute

At the Max Planck Institute in Germany, for example, scientists have succeeded in raising ten two-pound carp in one ten-gallon aquarium! The fish are so crowded that their backs are out of the water, and they are effectively unable to move more than an inch or so in any direction. In order to accomplish such a feat, vast amounts of energy must be used, as the temperature-

controlled water is continuously circulated, aerated, and filtered, and the fish fed a certain percentage of their weight each day with a ration of specially formulated food. When one considers the real cost of such an operation, it becomes obvious that these fish dinners are a "heat sink," i.e., they require more energy to produce than they give back in food.

The Real Costs

It is for this reason that we are extremely skeptical when we hear of schemes for raising trout in urban basements. The environmental cost of the electricity required to continuously pump, filter and control the temperature of the water, not to mention the fact that commercial fish chows are largely derived from other fish caught in foreign waters (how many Peruvians are suffering a protein-deficient diet because Americans like to eat trout?), make such schemes as environmentally unsound as the worst agribusiness practices.

Filtration Aeration &

Fish in close confinement, as anyone who has ever raised tropical fish knows, require constantly aerated and filtered water to survive. Just as a large number of people confined in a small, tightly closed room would quickly become sick in the stale air unless adequate ventilation were provided, so a lot of fish in a small tank will suffer from lack of oxygen in their water. In addition to this, fish crowded in a small space will excrete growth-inhibiting chemicals called metabolites which prevent normal growth no matter how much the fish are fed. For this reason, their water must be filtered.

To accomplish these functions in a closed system, the water must be circulated rapidly enough to filter out the metabolites as fast as they are produced, and replace the oxygen as fast as it is used up. This generally means the use of large amounts of electricity, and as we have already pointed out elsewhere, the 20 kilowatt-hour per month output of our wind-electric system is not enough to meet this demand.

Fish also require certain minimum levels
of temperature if they are to put on much growth.
U.S. Department of Agriculture Bulletin #2244,
<u>Catfish Farming</u>, states:

> "Catfish grow rapidly if
> properly fed and if the water
> temperature is 70° F. or more.
> Growth is slow between 60°
> and 70° F. Little growth occurs
> when water is colder than 60° F."

Trout, on the other hand, are cold water fish
which don't thrive in temperatures much higher
than 60° F. Since part of the rationale of aquaculture in an eco-system greenhouse is to provide a passive heating system, warm water fish
are the type we want to raise. This requires a
solar panel large enough to heat the volume of
our tank to the temperature requirements of the
fish species we wish to culture. We have already
mentioned that the 100 square feet of collector
that we estimate would be necessary to keep our
1400-gallon tank between 70° and 80° F. would
cost between $500.00 and $1300.00 at current
off-the-shelf prices, although we could make
one for much less than that.

Fish must be fed, and since the ecologically
disastrous commercial fish chows are out of the

question, that means we must produce our own food. Carniverous fish, like bluegill, trout and catfish, require a high protein diet of insects, earthworms, aquatic invertebrates, etc., which can be cultivated. Herbiverous fish, like Tilapia and Amurs, will thrive on a diet of algae, aquatic plants, and even carrot tops.

Carniverous Fish

Our initial experiments were with carniverous fish. The program called for about 100 catfish fingerlings to be planted in the fish tank, but limited finances - coupled with the unavailability of commercially raised catfish in lots of less than 1000 - necessitated an alternative plan. Consequently, in May, 1974, we filed the barbs off several fish hooks, half filled two 55-gallon drums with water, and set off in our Volkswagen bus for the nearest pond, about 40 miles away. Within two hours we managed to catch 55 bluegill sunfish which we quickly transported home and stocked in our 1400-gallon tank. The fish survived the transplant in good order, with no casualties.

Earthworms

In a letter from Dr. McLarney we learned that recent research by other experts has suggested that earthworms are superior nutritionally to commercial trout and catfish rations, so we were on good grounds in using them to feed our bluegills. Further encouragement came from Philip and Joyce Mahan, authors of an article entitled "Raising Catfish in a Barrel," which appeared in the November 1973 issue of Organic Gardening & Farming and which described an

Photo 18   Son Clayton with 9½ inch Sunfish

earthworm feeding system for catfish. Since
we already had four 55-gallon drum-halves
planted with earthworms and compost, we felt
we were well on our way toward becoming fish
farmers.

Then, what we call the "free lunch rule"
began to assert itself. (It's a basic truth of
ecology that "there is no such thing as a free
lunch") ... and indeed, in working with our little
eco-system, we have had that law enforced on
us many times. The fact is inescapable: you
can't get something for nothing.

What happened was that the
fish were constantly hungry. The
more we fed them, the more they
ate, until our supply of earthworms
couldn't keep up with the demand.
Then we reread the Mahan article
and learned that the authors are
commercial earthworm raisers
... an extremely significant fact that we hadn't
previously considered.

Obviously, our four little compost bins were
totally inadequate for producing the number of
worms we needed. If one figures a minimum
growth diet of five worms per fish per day, one
finds he is using - assuming 55 fish - 1,925 per
week, 7,700 per month and 46,200 every six
months. At a cost (in our area) of $20.00 per
7,000 earthworms, those fish dinners began to
be anything but a "free lunch." The long-term
solution, of course, is to create a much larger
worm farm ... one in which the creatures' natural reproduction is able to keep up with the
need for fish food.

Bug Light

Meanwhile, in an effort to ease the demand
on our hard-pressed earthworms, we attached
a 12-volt automobile taillight bulb to the wind-
electric system, hung it over the fish tank each
night during the summer, left the door and all
vent flaps open, and used the light to attract insects for the fish to eat. This system worked
very well. Although we were apprehensive about
bringing such visitors into the greenhouse, we
needn't have worried. The bluegills must have

gotten virtually every one of them, because we had no problems with insect damage to the plants. It became something of a pastime to "watch the fish eat." Each evening one could see them grouped in a huge circle around the light, waiting for any bug foolish enough to come within striking distance. Each morning a thin film of "leftovers" - insect wings, legs, etc. - covered the water.

That solution worked just fine for the summer months, but when the nights began to cool off and the bug population dwindled, it was back to an earthworm diet for the fishes. When we finally harvested the fish in the autumn of 1974 they had put on virtually no growth at all.

By then, of course, we'd learned that the wind-electric system couldn't handle the load for water circulation, but with a density of only one fish for each 25 gallons of water, we weren't overly worried about aeration and filtration.

Herbiverous Fish

For obvious reasons, our thoughts then turned to herbiverous fish. Tilapia seemed a good choice since, in addition to being plant eaters, they are extremely prolific. Another option was the White Amur, or grass carp, which is now available in this country from a few fish culturists. This species is a voracious plant eater, reaching weights of 70 pounds in a relatively short period of time. In addition, it is not temperature sensitive, and can survive in very cold water. (Tilapia

will die in water temperatures much below 50° F.)
Though we've never eaten Amur, they are said to
be a gourmet delicacy, prized for their flavor.
There is only one drawback
to this species - they will
not breed in captivity.

This left Tilapia as the only logical choice,
but since these fish can't live in cold water and
won't grow in water less than 70° F., it meant
some modifications to our whole set-up.

55-Gal. Drum Aquarium

After reading about the intensive carp culture experiments at the Max Planck Institute, we
decided to try a modified version of their technique. Instead of raising ten carp in a ten-gallon
aquarium, why couldn't we raise thirty Tilapia
in a 55-gallon drum? We reasoned that 55 gallons
was a small enough volume of water to be handled
by both the wind-electric system and the small
solar panel we originally employed. (This was
a "Solarator" swimming pool heater. The manufacturer states it will heat up to 10,000 gallons
of water but, perhaps significantly, he doesn't
state to what temperature.) Of course, 55 gallons of water wouldn't do much toward heating
the greenhouse, but by then we were only interested in making some method of aquaculture
work for us.

We decided to use the principle of the aquarium, familiar to tropical fish fanciers. A false
bottom, consisting of a round piece of corrugated
plastic roofing material, was placed in the 55-

gallon drum. This was equipped with four pieces
of pvc pipe - two to admit a constant stream of
compressed air, two to allow it to escape from
the bottom of the tank. A four-inch layer of
crushed oyster shell was placed on top of the
corrugated false bottom, and holes drilled at
one-inch intervals along the corrugations allowed
for the circulation of water. When compressed

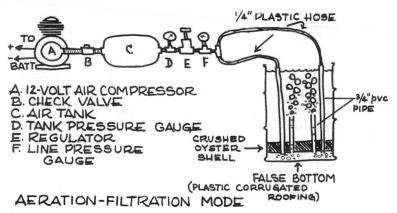

A. 12-VOLT AIR COMPRESSOR
B. CHECK VALVE
C. AIR TANK
D. TANK PRESSURE GAUGE
E. REGULATOR
F. LINE PRESSURE
        GAUGE

AERATION-FILTRATION MODE

Figure 13

air enters the system - in addition to providing
oxygen for the fish - it causes a "current" to
draw the water through the crushed oyster shell.
Aerobic bacteria living in this material devour
the growth-inhibiting metabolites produced by
the fish. For those readers unfamiliar with this
process, it is the same life-support system used
in home aquariums.

    Compressed air is provided by a 12-volt re-
creational vehicle air compressor. A valve on
the air tank meters out the small amount needed
to keep the system going. Since the compressor
shuts itself off when the tank pressure reaches
40 psi, it is not required to run all of the time.
When the tank pressure drops to 20 psi, the compressor automatically starts up again. If we

assume the 60-watt compressor runs only fifteen minutes every hour, we would only be drawing about 10.8 Kwh a month.

The tank is heated by a separate system. A thermostat placed at the solar panel automatically turns on a tiny 12-volt recreational vehicle water pump which pumps two gallons per minute, and only draws 18 watts. Water is pumped from the bottom of the tank when the solar panel thermostat registers 120° F. The pump is turned off when the solar panel temperature drops to 80° F.

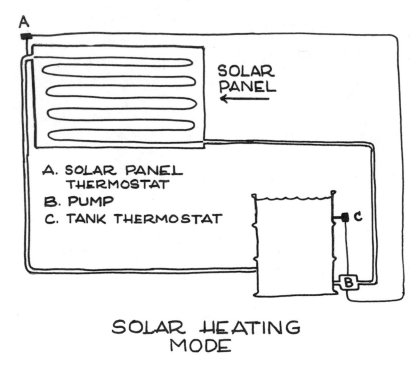

SOLAR HEATING
MODE

Figure 14

Another thermostat at the top of the tank shuts the entire system down when the tank temperature reaches 85° F. The system is activated again when the tank temperature drops to 70° F.

Now we must hasten to say that we never got quite this far with the idea, since the RV air compressor burned out the first day we hooked it up to a regular ten-gallon aquarium. (This was just a preliminary test to see how it worked.) Apparently 12-volt recreational vehicle equipment is not designed for continuous duty, and our disgust with all this technology, coupled with the fact that we no longer had any money to continue the project, caused us to abandon aquaculture for the time being.

It should be pointed out, however, that a larger wind-electric system, such as is described in the appendix to this book, should easily be capable of providing enough power to make the original aquaculture scheme feasible. Readers with a Rube Goldberg turn of mind (technology can be fun, despite the fact that it is killing us), will also note that the 55-gallon drum aquarium just described should work with the proper equipment.

Less energy intensive methods of aquaculture are being developed by the New Alchemy Institute, and while we have lost a lot of our original enthusiasm for the subject, the Alchemists are apparently having a measure of success.

ACCESS

For addresses of live fish suppliers, see the advertisements in such magazines as Aquaculture & The Fish Farmer, 201 Izard Street, Little Rock, Arkansas 72201.

FINAL THOUGHTS

In the preceding pages we have briefly outlined our two years' experience with a unique
concept in home food production. The weakest
link in the system, the wind-electric component,
in no way invalidates the concept itself. That
would be like saying that automobiles aren't feasible because we tried to power one with a lawn-
mower motor. With a more powerful wind generator, we are confident that we could make the
eco-system as fully productive as it was originally described in Vol. 28 of The Mother Earth
News.

Obviously much work remains to be done,
and many experiments made to hone the system
to an edge of maximum efficiency. While we unfortunately didn't keep a close record of our ex-
penditures, a 280 sq. ft. eco-system greenhouse
just like ours, including the wind-electric system,
should cost between $1,000.00 and $1,500.00 for
materials and equipment. (It is assumed that the
owner does his own construction.) An attached
greenhouse of about 150 sq. ft. should run between $200.00 and $300.00 for building materials alone. It is difficult to give more than very
rough cost estimates, since individual circumstances vary widely. We hope that in these pages
we have inspired others to construct their own
eco-systems, and help us to carry the idea for-
ward and bring it to perfection.

We must mention, however, what many readers have probably thought about already, and that is: how much non-renewable energy is used in producing the technology that comprises the ecosystem? Wind generators, batteries, fluorescent tubes, fibreglas greenhouse material and cement blocks are all items made in factories, and all require fossil fuels in their manufacture. While it is true that the drift of this sort of thinking, carried to its logical extreme, would require the purist to live in a cave and subsist by hunting and gathering, we should not lose sight of the fact that it takes energy to create energy-saving devices. To us the problem is not whether wind generators are practical - they are - the question that bothers us is whether the corporate frame of reference, which seems necessary to the manufacture of wind electric machines and their components, is healthy for the world eco-system. This takes us back to the thought raised in the introduction to this volume: that the roots of all our problems are more moral and political than anything else. All of the alternative energy systems in the world will count for very little unless we can change the way in which we perceive ourselves and our environment. It isn't a matter of replacing one energy source with another, or exchanging types of hardware - the crux of the problem is how we perceive ourselves and our world. That is a question that each individual must answer for himself, and it is the aggregate of individual answers which will determine nothing less than how we shall live in the future.

James B. DeKorne
El Rito, New Mexico
September 29, 1975

REFERENCES CITED

INTRODUCTORY CONCEPTS

1. The editors, Energy Primer, Portola
    Institute, 1974, p. 179

2. Anonymous, Famine - Can We Survive?
    Ambassador College Press, Pasadena,
    1974, p. 52

3. F. H. King, Farmers of Forty Centuries,
    (1911 edition republished by Rodale Press,
    Emmaus, Pa.), p. 193

4. J. B. DeKorne, "Build Your Own Eco-
    system," The Mother Earth News, Vol. 28,
    p. 68

GREENHOUSE BASICS

1. Ken Kern, The Owner Built Homestead,
    reprinted in Vol. #16 of The Mother Earth
    News, p. 78

2. K. Taylor and E. Gregg, Winter Flowers
    in Greenhouse and Sun-heated Pit, Chas.
    Scribner's Sons, New York, 1969, pp. 14,
    56

PHOTOPERIOD

1. E. Chabot, Greenhouse Gardening For
    Everyone, M. Barrows & Co., Inc.,
    New York, 1946

2. E. F. Maas and R. M. Adamson, Soilless
    Culture of Commercial Greenhouse
    Tomatoes, Canada Dept. of Agriculture
    publication #1460, Ottawa, 1972, p. 7

3. H. M. Cathey and L. E. Campbell, "Lamps and Lighting - a horticultural view," *Lighting Design and Application*, Nov. 1974

4. S. H. Wittwer and S. Honma, *Greenhouse Tomatoes - Guidelines for Successful Production*, Michigan State University Press, East Lansing, 1969, p. 10

5. M. Hackleman, *Wind & Windspinners*, Earthmind, Saugus, Calif. , 1974, p. 105

6. The editors, *Encyclopedia of Organic Gardening*, Rodale Press, Emmaus, Pa. , 1969, p. 365

CARBON DIOXIDE

1. S. H. Witter and S. Honma, op. cit.

2. M. Saxton, personal communication with the author

HYDROPONICS

1. D. Mendola, *Energy Primer*, Portola Institute, Menlo Park, 1974, p. 135

2. Sneed, et. al. , "Fish Farming and Hydroponics," *Aquaculture and The Fish Farmer*, May/June, 1975, p. 18

3. L. D. Weiss, "Hydroponic Gardening," *The Tribal Messenger*, 30 April - 14 May, 1973

AQUACULTURE

1. W. McLarney, "Aquaculture on the Organic Farm and Homestead," *Organic Gardening & Farming*, August, 1971

2. R. Rodale, "Editorial," *Organic Gardening and Farming*, April, 1971

AQUACULTURE (cont'd.)

3. R. Grizzel, Jr., et. al., <u>Catfish Farming,
    a New Farm Crop</u>, USDA Farmer's Bulle-
    tin # 2244, 1969, p. 5

4. P. and J. Mahan, "Raising Catfish in a
    Barrel," <u>Organic Gardening and Farming</u>,
    November, 1973

RECOMMENDED READING

1. J. Bardach, et. al., <u>Aquaculture</u>, Wiley-
    Interscience, New York, 1972

2. J. S. Douglas, <u>Beginners Guide to Hydro-
    ponics</u>, Drake Publishers, Inc., New York,
    1973

3. D. Newcomb, <u>The Postage Stamp Garden
    Book</u>, J. P. Tarcher, Inc., Los Angeles,
    1975

4. S. Spotte, <u>Fish and Invertebrate Culture</u>,
    Wiley-Interscience, New York, 1970

5. <u>Journal #2</u> of The New Alchemists, New
    Alchemy Institute, Box 432, Woods Hole,
    Mass. 02543

APPENDIX I

DO—IT—YOURSELF WIND GENERATORS

Whenever anyone tells me that he wants to install a wind generator on his homestead, my first advice is: buy a new one if you can afford it. Unfortunately, most of us who have returned to the land are in no position to lay out over $2,000.00 for a new high-wattage wind generator. (Indeed, I have been told that recent fluctuations of the value of the U.S. dollar on the world money market have driven the price of a new Dunlite unit to over twice that amount.)

My second best advice is: if you can't afford a new machine, try to locate a used one and re-build it. Just about anywhere in the rural Great Plains states wind generators were common sights on farms during the 1930s and 40s. When the REA finally strung its wires to these localities, the generators were often taken down and sold for scrap. Occasionally, however, after a lot of back road driving and many conversations with farmers old enough to remember them, one can still find a few of these generators still standing. (Usually they weren't taken down because most people aren't into the hair-raising job of working with upwards of 500 pounds of machinery while tied onto the top of a high tower - an experience roughly analogous to removing an engine from an automobile while 45 feet up in the air!)

The two most common wind generators were the Wincharger and the Jacobs - respectively the Chevrolet and Rolls Royce of homestead wind-electric plants. The Wincharger came in several models, from six to 110 volts, and from 200 to 1500 watts. The Jacobs, a much heavier machine, was built in 32 and 110 volt configurations, and ranged from 1500 to 3000 watts. The 32 volt models of both makes were the most popular in their day, and of the two makes, the Wincharger is the brand you're most likely to encounter now. The Jacobs is quite rare nowadays, but a real find if you turn one up in reasonably good condition.

Almost any old wind generator you may locate is more likely than not in need of extensive restoration. It is unusual to find one that still has usable rotors - these, being made of wood (with the exception of some later models of the Wincharger, which had aluminum rotors) are the first parts to deteriorate. After all, the machine has probably stood untended for well over 25 years of summer thunder storms and winter blizzards! It is even rarer yet to find one that still has the original control box, though these can be made up by most any electrician worth his salt.

Is it worthwhile to try to restore one of these old wind-electric plants? Most definitely yes! If you are selective, and can locate a machine that doesn't have unrepairable damage, such as broken castings or major parts missing, a little bit of enjoyable restoration will reward you with up to 3000 watts of "free" electricity. Anyone who has rebuilt a Model A Ford, or likes to fool around with old cars, will feel right at home tearing into a 1940s vintage wind generator.

Unfortunately, however, used wind generators in rebuildable condition aren't all that easy to find. That leaves us with choice number three - home-built wind generators. It is the author's

opinion that most of the do-it-yourself machines
that he has seen and read about weren't worth
the time and money spent to build them. Does
this mean that homemade machines aren't practical? Not necessarily so - in the following pages
I will attempt to describe the limitations of these
machines and outline possible ways in which
these limitations might be overcome.

**How big
a wind
generator?**

It has been estimated that the average American home uses 10 kilowatt hours of electricity
per day.[1] That's about 300 Kwh per month. The
Clews homestead uses 110 Kwh per month with a
new 2 Kw, 115 volt Dunlite wind generator. Most
home-built wind generators are made from 12
volt automobile alternators or generators which
are rated at about 500 watts or 1/2 Kw. If a new
2 Kw machine gives roughly 100 Kwh per month,
then it follows (assuming similar wind conditions)
that a 1/2 Kw machine will give about 25 Kwh
per month, or less than 1 Kwh per day and less
than one-tenth of the American average consumption. And there you have limitation number one - home-built wind generators using automotive components (assuming they can be constructed to operate at peak efficiency - which we
shall see is a big assumption), still don't put out
enough power to equal one-tenth of what most
Americans consider "normal."

Now, I would be the first person to say that
we should all revise our conception of what is
"normal" electrical consumption - lest anyone
should take me to task, let it be known that I
have deliberately lived without any outside
source of electricity at all for over three years.
The point I am trying to make here is that if we
are going to go to wind-generated electricity,

we should shoot for something capable of power-
ing more than a few 25 watt bulbs. We are, after
all, advocating an enlightened technology, not a
return to the 19th century.

Which generator?   I have always felt that (with the exception of
specialized applications) wind generators of un-
der 1000 watt capacity are impractical for most
people's needs. Since electrical devices designed
for automotive usage are not really adequate for
the needs of a modern homestead, we can look
more profitably in the direction of surplus aircraft equipment to build our wind generator.
For example, on page 57 of the Palley Supply Co.
catalog (see Bibliography), a firm dealing in
surplus military and industrial equipment of all
sorts, we see listed (among many others) a surplus aircraft generator (#G-1273-1A) which produces 75 amps at 24-32 volts. Since volts times
amps equals watts, we deduce that this unit is
capable of putting out about 2400 watts. (That's
400 more watts than a standard Dunlite machine!)
This unit weighs 31 pounds and costs about $30.00.

        In using the Dunlite unit as a comparison,
I don't mean to imply that this aircraft generator
is "better" because it puts out more power - it
most certainly is not of comparable quality since,
for one thing, it weighs but a fraction of the Dunlite machine. 31 pounds compared with 400
pounds indicates that the Dunlite Company's engi-
neers designed their unit for a lifetime of efficient, trouble-free operation as a wind-driven
machine, and that the aircraft generator was designed for high output at high rpm and minimum
weight. Since aircraft are torn down periodically for maintenance and replacement of parts,
the above generator was not expected to last for

more than a specified number of hours of operation. This is limitation number two of a home-
made wind electric system - one is of necessity
required to make use of generators which were
never designed for the unique conditions of wind
power. The same conditions hold true for automotive adaptations, of course, so we're still
ahead by going to the higher wattage aircraft
generators; we just can't expect it to hold up as
long as a unit designed specifically for wind use.

The generator just mentioned puts out its
rated power between 1800 and 2500 rpm, so we
know that we are going to have to gear it up.
This is necessary because even a well-designed
and carefully built rotor ('propeller') will turn
at only about 150 to 300 rpm. This confronts us
with limitation number three: "the maximum
power that a wind turbine can get from the wind
passing through the disk area of its blades is 57
percent of the wind energy."[2] It has also been
estimated that any gearing device will eat up
another 15% of the available power. These limitations, of course, are true for any wind generator, but it behooves us to be aware of them so
that we can design our unit to make efficient use
of the 42% of (free) power remaining to us. Clearly,
the rotor and generator characteristics must be
matched to produce the best effect.[3] A step-up
ratio of 1:10 rotor speed to generator speed should
be sufficient to give us the output we need.

**Gearing and
lubrication**

At this point we should look at some existing
wind generators, both commercially manufactured
and home-made, to see what we can learn from
them. Most of the Jacobs machines, probably
the best homestead wind-electric plants ever
manufactured, were direct-drive units - they

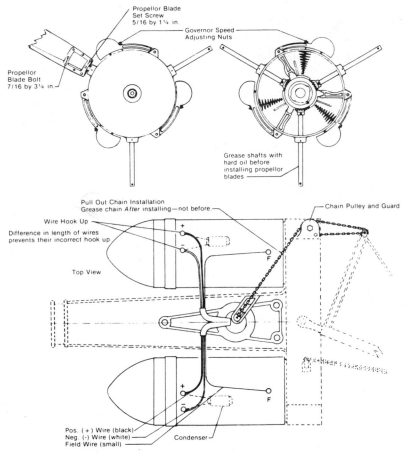

Propeller Blade
Set Screw
5/16 by 1¼ in.

Governor Speed
Adjusting Nuts

Propellor
Blade Bolt
7/16 by 3¼ in.

Grease shafts with
hard oil before
installing propellor
blades

Pull Out Chain Installation
Grease chain *After* installing—not before.

Chain Pulley and Guard

Wire Hook Up

Difference in length of wires
prevents their incorrect hook up

Top View

Pos. (+) Wire (black)
Neg. (-) Wire (white)
Field Wire (small)

Condenser

Figure 15   Top view of Jacobs Model 15.

were designed to put out usable amounts of electricity at the relatively slow speeds of the rotor.
To do this required an extremely heavy generator - the 2500 watt Jacobs unit which I own probably weighs in the neighborhood of 500 pounds.
(It took four strong men to lift it into my pickup
truck, and even then it was not an easy job.)

The old Winchargers, on the other hand, were
gear-driven units and much lighter in weight.
They didn't produce as many watts as the Jacobs,
and because of their more "complicated" design,

with gears and consequently higher generator rpm's, they didn't last as long. I have been told that, with the exception of occasional brush replacement, the Jacobs was designed to give a lifetime of trouble-free operation. This only stands to reason, given the relationships between friction, speed and time, a slow-speed generator will last longer than a high speed unit.

Counting the number of gear teeth on a Wincharger I own, I have determined that its gear ratio is about 1:8. These gears are enclosed in a cast-iron housing and turn in a bath of specially formulated light-weight oil, which is changed yearly. The Dunlite machine operates on a similar principle, although they claim that oil changes are necessary at only 5 year intervals.

Now, what about our home-built unit - how are we going to gear it up? The November, 1972 issue of Popular Science magazine (page 103) has an article and plans for a do-it-yourself wind generator. In looking at these plans we see that a 1:9 gear ratio was achieved by making use of mini-bike sprockets and drive-chain. At first glance, this appears to be the solution to our problem - until we realize that the plans make no provision for an oil bath to lubricate the system. Such a design would necessitate frequent trips up the tower to oil the gears and chain. Unless you enjoy frequent machine maintenance and tower climbing, this system is impractical.

Volume #20 of The Mother Earth News (page 32) has another home-built design created by Jim Sencenbaugh of Palo Alto, California. While his wind generator in all other respects looks like a well-designed and efficient unit, we see that the gearing also makes use of mini-bike components, with no apparent oil-bath provision.

The New Alchemy Institute of Woods Hole, Massachusetts, has a wind generator which makes use of an automobile differential mounted on a high tower. The rotor is placed where one wheel hub used to be, and turns an automobile alternator at the drive-shaft spline. Again, this appears to be a solution to our gearing problem until we realize that the lowest commonly available auto differential gear ratios are in the neighborhood of 1:4 - not nearly enough to get good performance from our aircraft generator. Of course, we can place a mini-bike gear-up at the drive-shaft spline, but we still haven't solved our problem, because those mini-bike chains will still need lubrication. A gear box for the chains and sprockets could be fabricated, but probably not without some difficulty. On the other hand, a small transmission from a motorcycle or mini-bike might provide adequate gearing here. Bear in mind, however, that the wind energy that is lost in gear friction doesn't generate any electricity, and the more friction we have the less efficient our system will be. Obviously, then, the fewer gears, chains and sprockets we use, the better.

One possible way out of our gearing dilemma may be found in the design of the Jacobs Model 15 wind generator. As was mentioned earlier, most Jacobs machines were direct-drive units which had no gearing at all. The Model 15, however, made use of a fly-wheel which turned two small 750 watt generators. (See reproductions from Model 15 owner's manual.) The rotor turned a short drive-shaft to which the flywheel was attached. The flywheel was encased in a housing

to which the two generators were bolted. If you
can imagine an automobile bell housing that has
two starter motors bolted to it, one on each side
of the engine, you can get an idea of what the
Model 15 looks like. In this case, of course, generators replace the starter motors, and instead
of an engine with its crank-shaft, there is a
short drive-shaft connecting the rotor to the flywheel. If this sounds confusing, look at the diagrams - the device is amazingly simple.

In addition to solving our gearing and lubrication problems (the housing contains an oil
bath), this design gives us an added bonus - two
generators! If we welded up an oil-tight housing, obtained a suitable flywheel from a junked
auto engine, geared it properly to two of our
aircraft generators (suitable gears could be
machined or scrounged from auto parts), we
would have a wind generator capable of producing 4800 watts of power! The closest thing you
can buy commercially that puts out this much
power is the Elektro WV 35 GT 4,000 watt machine, which costs more than $6,000.00.

Now, I have never constructed such a generator myself, but the Jacobs Company used to
make them, and the principle is a valid one. A
housing could be fabricated from 1/4-inch steel
plate. Installation of a "rear main" bearing
would be the most complicated part of the job,
but anyone reasonably proficient with an arc
welder should be able to do it. The shaft from
the rotor is supported by two pillow blocks on a
brace, which could be made out of 4- or 6-inch
channel iron. There is nothing in the design beyond the skills of any moderately advanced back-
yard mechanic. The cost of construction should

be very little, if any, more than some of the other designs available at this time.

Our wind generator, in theory at least, has overcome the two main drawbacks of home-built wind electric plants: low wattage and complicated gearing to gain the necessary rpm's required by generators designed for automotive or aircraft application. Our task is not yet completed, however - there are many other factors which must be taken into consideration in constructing a highly efficient unit.

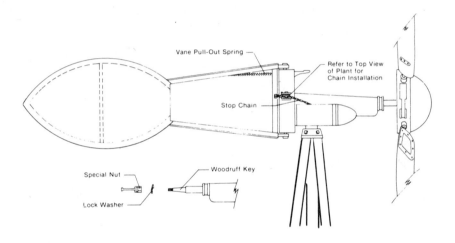

Figure 16   Right side view of Jacobs Model 15 (Twin Motor Electric).

The rotor   The propeller, or more accurately, the rotor (propellers are devices used to "propel" aircraft), is in some respects the heart of the whole system. If our rotor is not designed and built so as to take maximum advantage of the power in the wind, we can't expect to get much performance from our generator. Again, we can look at other wind generators to get ideas for our home-built unit.

The Jacobs machines had three wooden rotor blades which, when turning in the wind, gave a total rotor diameter of fifteen feet. It has been calculated that, when turning at 225 rpm, the weight of the entire rotor is something like 1100 pounds. Obviously, balancing is of utmost importance for any rotor system we use, or vibration would soon tear the whole unit apart. [4]

The Winchargers used two and four-bladed rotors. The early four-bladed units and, to the best of my knowledge, all of the two-bladed units were made of wood. Rotor diameter on the large units was either 12 or 13 feet, depending on the model. (The Wincharger Company manufactured many different models - I presently own three complete units and have parts for many more, yet no two of them are exactly alike, although parts are often interchangeable from model to model.) The two-bladed rotors are essentially a 12-foot 2 X 6 plank which has been worked into the proper aerodynamic shape. Any careful workman, proficient with simple wood-working tools, should be able to duplicate such a rotor with ease.

A more sophisticated rotor design, making use of an expandable paper product called Hexcel, which is covered with fibreglas, is described on page 105 of the November, 1972 issue of Popular Science magazine. This is a three-bladed rotor of the Jacobs type. An experimental two-bladed "sail-wing" design is shown on page 71 of the same issue. Complete diagrams for building your own two-bladed wooden rotor are found on pages 47-50 of Volume #3 of Lifestyle magazine. Plans for Jim Sencenbaugh's complete home-built wind generator (including 3-bladed rotor),

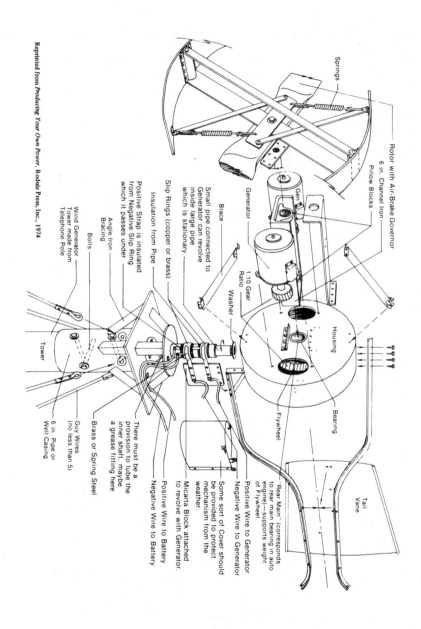

Springs

Rotor with Air-Brake Governor
6 in. Channel Iron

Pillow Blocks

Generator

Gen

Brace

Small pipe connected to
Generator can revolve
inside large pipe
which is stationary.

Slip Rings (copper or brass)

Insulation from Pipe

Positive Strap is insulated
from Negative Slip Ring
which it passes under.

Wind Generator
Tower made from
Telephone Pole

Angle Iron
Bracing

Bolts

Tower

1:10 Gear
Ratio

Washer

6 in. Pipe or
Well Casing

Guy Wires
(no less than 5)

Brass or Spring Steel

There must be a
provision to lube the
inner shaft, maybe
a grease fitting here

Flywheel

Housing

Bearing

Negative Wire to Battery

Positive Wire to Battery

Micarta Block attached
to revolve with Generator.

Some sort of Cover should
be provided to protect
mechanism from the
weather.

Negative Wire to Generator

Positive Wire to Generator

"Rear Main" (corresponds
to rear main bearing in auto
engine)—supports weight
of Flywheel.

Tail
Vane

Figure 17   Home-built 4,800-watt generator, blown apart to show
construction details.

as described in Volume #20 of The Mother Earth
News, are available for about $15.00. (See biblio-
graphy at end of chapter.)

There seem to be some differences of opinion about the ideal number of blades a rotor
should have. E. W. Golding, in his definitive
book, The Generation of Electricity by Wind
Power (out of print), states that studies made by
the War Production Board during World War II
found that the best number of blades is two. [5]
These studies, however, were concerned with
very large generators to be used for the commercial production of electricity. Most of the
homestead-sized generators available today,
such as the Dunlite machine, make use of a
three-bladed rotor.

In an interview with Marcellus Jacobs (the
man who designed and manufactured the fine
Jacobs wind generator) in Volume #24 of The
Mother Earth News, the advantages of the three-
bladed rotor are clearly brought out.

For the purposes of our home-built wind
generator, however, a two-bladed rotor has two
advantages which we should consider: first, a
wooden rotor, like the Winchargers used, is easy
to make; and second, such a rotor design lends
itself to being coupled with an airbrake governor, which is also easy to make.

A governing device is absolutely necessary,
of course, to slow the rotor down in high winds
to prevent damage to the machine. All of the
two-bladed Winchargers made use of an airbrake governor - a device which bolted to the
front of the rotor in a position perpendicular to
the blades. (See Figure 19). If you can imagine

153

two giant automobile brake shoes held under
spring tension on either end of a steel rod, you
get a rough picture of what an airbrake governor looks like. At "normal" wind speeds, the
spring tension holds the shoes so that they do
not interfere with the speed of the rotor. At
high wind speeds, centrifugal force overcomes
the spring tension, and the "brake shoes" are
pulled outward so that they drag through the air
and slow the speed of the rotor. For $1.45,
Popular Mechanics magazine sells plans for a
wind generator which makes use of such a governor. Ask for plan #X796 (see bibliography).

Reprinted from *Producing Your Own Power*, Rodale Press, Inc., 1974

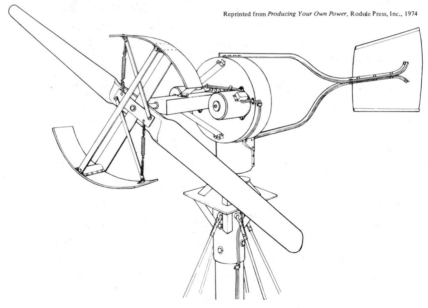

Figure 18   Home-built generator based on Jacobs Model 15, capable of
producing about 4,800 watts.

If we take the two-bladed rotor design as
described in Lifestyle #3, extend its dimensions
proportionately to make a 14-foot long rotor
(plans describe a seven-footer), and couple with
that an airbrake governor (also scaled up to con-

form to the 14-foot length) as is described in the
Popular Mechanics plans, we will have a rotor
and governor unit which should work reasonably
well with the two aircraft generators we built in
our copy of the Jacobs Model 15.

The tail

Our wind generator now needs a tail vane -
a relatively simple device which keeps the machine oriented so that it is always facing the
wind. A tail vane from an old wind pump (commonly called "windmills," despite the fact that
they pump water rather than grind grain) can
easily be adapted to fit our wind generator. Both
the Jacobs and Wincharger machines had tail
vanes which were designed to be movable - that
is, by turning a crank at the base of the tower,
the vane could be brought from a position perpendicular to the plane of the rotor to an orien-
tation parallel with it. This had the effect of
turning the machine "out of the wind," a man-
euver carried out when extremely high winds
were expected, or when the batteries were fully
charged. Virtually all wind pump vanes are designed to operate the same way, and could be
adapted to our generator with little trouble.
Should a wind pump vane not be readily available,
both the Popular Mechanics and Sencenbaugh plans
describe how to construct one.

Our generator must be free to turn in any
direction in order to capture the full power in
the wind. (Although many locations have "prevailing winds," it is actually not true that winds
always come from a single direction.)[6] A bearing
could be constructed for our purposes out of the
wheel bearings and hub from an automobile axle -
the Popular Science design utilizes those off a
Volkswagen. The older versions of the Wincharger,

however, had no "bearings" at all - the supporting shaft consisted of a shaft or "pipe" which fit snugly inside a slightly larger pipe. The outside section had a grease fitting which provided for lubrication (usually at six-month intervals). Visualize one pipe fitting inside another with a film of grease lubricating them and you have the idea. The LeJay Manual describes this sort of "bearing" as do the Sencenbaugh plans. For ease of construction, this method is probably superior to the automobile wheel bearing idea. (Bear in mind that our wind machine will never be required to pivot anywhere near as fast or often as a car wheel turns, and so a highly sophisticated bearing is not mandatory.)

The commutator

More complicated, but not nearly as complicated as everyone seems to think, is the construction of a slip-ring commutator. This is a device which allows current to be transmitted from the constantly shifting generator to the stationary wires which run down the tower to the batteries. Many plans for home-made wind generators just allow the wires to twist around the tower - a slipshod compromise which calls into question the validity of the rest of the design. Slip-ring commutators are no big deal - both the Popular Mechanics and Sencenbaugh plans show how they are constructed.

The tower

We are now finished with the generator and its components, and are ready to consider our tower. Any wind pump tower of suitable height is easily adapted for wind generator use, but if one is not available, an old telephone pole can also be used; just be sure that the pole is guyed with no fewer than five cables. (That way, if one snaps, you still have four cables to hold the tower

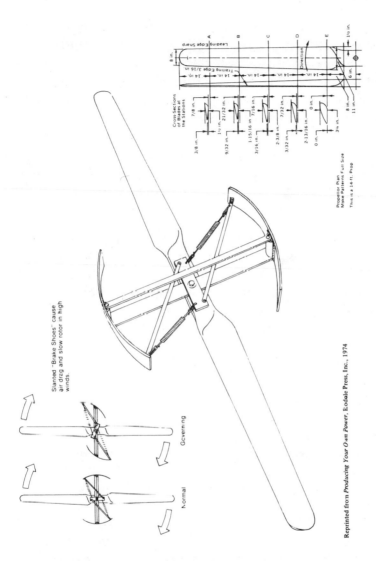

Figure 19   Two-bladed rotor with brake shoes.

in place until you can replace the broken one.) Provision must be made at the top of the tower to hold the generator and its pivoting mechanism. This is easily accomplished by shaving the end of the pole down so that it will just accept a 2-

foot length of 6" steel pipe of at least 1/4" wall thickness. At least two (four would be better) long bolts hold the steel pipe to the pole at top and bottom. The bolts should be perpendicular to each other. A square piece of 3/8" or 1/2" steel plate is welded to the top of the pipe, and braced with four pieces of angle iron welded to the pipe's sides. (See Figure 17). On top of this "platform" is attached the generator's pivoting mechanism and slip-ring commutators and, to that, of course, is attached the generator.

One very important consideration must be borne in mind when erecting the tower. Most of the criticism of the unsatisfactory operation of a wind-driven plant is due to plants being installed in unsuitable positions or on low towers. No plant will work unless it is in a clear air stream and, if a person is not prepared to have a tower of suitable height, it is better not to install the plant. Even if the unit is installed on a clear plain or on top of a hill, it should never be on a tower of less than thirty feet. For all other conditions, a height of at least forty feet is recommended. [7]

Batteries

Our 24 volt, 4800 watt wind generator is now almost complete. Since the specifications on our aircraft generators state that they have a variable voltage (24 to 32 volts), we will rate the machine at 24 volts, and plan our battery package accordingly - i.e., twelve 2 volt, four 6 volt, or two 12 volt cells hooked up in series to provide 24 volts. It is interesting to note that the data plate on my 32 volt Jacobs machine gives its voltage as 40. This is standard procedure, so we don't have to worry that we are harming the 24 volt batteries when our home-built generator is charging at 32 volts. To the best of my knowledge, all DC generators are over-rated a few volts to insure full charge to the batteries. (e.g.: "12 volt" automobile generators actually put out 13 or 14 volts.)

Because of this relatively "low" voltage (as compared with standard house current of 110-120 volts), we will need some fairly heavy wire to carry the current. The old 32 volt Wincharger and Jacobs manuals recommend number six wire when the distance from the generator to the batteries is less than 100 feet; number four wire was used when the distance was 100 to 200 feet. However, distances longer than 100 feet are not recommended.

What sort of batteries are best? There are several options here - 2 volt industrial batteries of 180 amp hour rating or higher are available from any battery manufacturer. Jim Sencenbaugh states that "the use of golf cart batteries (Gould PB220, 6 volt 220 amp hour costing $35.00 each), are perhaps the best buy in terms of an inexpensive deep cycling unit."[8] Henry Clews' Solar Wind Company sells Australian house lighting batteries especially designed for wind generator use. Whatever you do, don't use standard automotive batteries - they were never designed for the special conditions under which you will be using them.

24 volt electric motors are readily available as military surplus, but for any other applications for your wind generated electricity you will need a 24 volt DC to 110 volt AC inverter. Such devices are described in Chapter 1 of Producing Your Own Power, Rodale Press, Inc. 1974.

A 24 volt voltage regulator will need to be constructed to regulate the battery charging rate. I doubt if a surplus voltage regulator from, say, some 24 volt military vehicle would be adequate to handle the high amperage from our two aircraft generators. If you are not knowledgeable about electronic devices, any competent electrician should be able to wire up a suitable voltage regulator for you.

Our do-it-yourself wind generator is now complete. I have not described many of the construction procedures in greater detail because such procedures are more than adequately described elsewhere. The bibliography at the end of this section is highly recommended reading for those wishing to build this or any wind generator. Anyone with a modest degree of mechanical aptitude should have little difficulty in constructing the machine I have just described. The best part is that, instead of the 1/2 kilowatt machines that most do-it-yourselfers create, this one is capable of 4.8 kilowatts - a lot more return on your time and money investment.

FOOTNOTES

1. Reines, Robt., "Wind Energy," Life Support Technics Conference Proceedings, Ghost Ranch, Abiquiu, N. M., 10/31/72, p. 20

2. Kidd, S. & Garr, D., "Electric Power from Windmills?", Popular Science, Nov. 1972, p. 72

3. Golding, E. E., The Generation of Electricity by Wind Power, Philosophical Library, New York, 1956, p. 235

4. Reines, op. cit. p. 20

5. Golding, op. cit. p. 210

6. Ibid, p. 58

7. Information taken from Dunlite tower installation pamphlet

8. Sencenbaugh, J., in personal letter to the author

ANNOTATED BIBLIOGRAPHY

Listed by Publication

Alternative Sources of Energy magazine, $5./yr. from: Don Marier, Rt. 2 - Box 90-A, Milaca, Mn. 56353. Bimonthly. (Some back issues available). See specifically:

Vol. #10, March 1973:
1. "High Speed Wind Generator," Bill Smith, p. 9
2. "Balancing the Blades," Ted Ledger, p. 17
3. "Balancing the Blades," Lyman Greenlee, p. 18

Vol. #12, Oct. - Nov. 1973:
1. "Some Notes on Windmills," Don Marier, p. 2

LeJay Manual, LeJay Mfg. Co., Belle Plaine, Mn.
    56011. This booklet is useful for its de-
    scription of slip-ring commutators, rotors,
    vanes, etc.

Lifestyle! magazine, P.O. Box 2300, Henderson-
    ville, N.C. 28739, See specifically:
    Vol. #3, pp. 47-51, particularly "Build a
        Wind Generator!", by Winnie Redrocker.
        Originally published in A.S.E. Vol. #8,
        describes how to construct a two-
        bladed wooden rotor.

Mother Earth News, P.O. Box 70, Hendersonville,
    N.C. 28739, see specifically:

1. Vol. #17, "Free Power from the Wind," Ed
    Trunk, p. 60;
2. Vol. #20, "I Built a Wind Generator for
    $400.00!", Jim Sencenbaugh, p. 32;
3. Vol. #24, "The Plowboy Interview - Mar-
    cellus Jacobs," p. 52;
    In the same issue: "The Answer is Blowin'
    in the Wind," J.B. DeKorne. Contains
    drawings and photographs of both home-
    built wind generators and the old Jacobs
    and Wincharger machines.

Palley Supply Co. Catalog - available for $1. from
    the Palley Supply Co., 2263 E. Vernon Ave.,
    Dept. M-70, Los Angeles, Calif., 90058. Source
    of surplus aircraft generators.

Popular Mechanics magazine, catalog of plans,
    publications, projects available for 25¢ from:
    Popular Mechanics, Dept. C, Box 1014, Radio
    City, N.Y., 10019. Source of plans for wind
    generators - most important, how to construct
    air-brake governors and slip-ring commuta-
    tors.

APPENDIX II

THE ATTACHED GREENHOUSE

Our eco-system, as mentioned previously, was originally inspired by the Lama Grow-hole, which itself is an adaptation of the old pit-greenhouse concept. Underground forcing structures are so much more energy efficient than traditional greenhouses that we would never even consider the latter type - with one notable exception. The so-called attached solar greenhouse, built against the south wall of a dwelling, while not as well insulated as a pit greenhouse, can, with proper management, provide a significant amount of heat to a home in the wintertime.

The secret lies in the venting system. Since warm air rises, a vent at the top of the north wall of the greenhouse spills excess heat into the house, while a vent near the bottom of the wall allows the cooler air from the dwelling to enter the greenhouse. During the night, the roles reverse and the heat from the house warms the greenhouse; a small wood-burning heater can also be used to heat the forcing structure.

The accompanying drawings, which originally appeared in Vol. #36 of The Mother Earth News, show the basic idea. We feel that this greenhouse design, in addition to being inexpensive to build, would be perfectly adaptable to the eco-system concepts as outlined in this book. Just be sure that you build an auxiliary system to ventilate the greenhouse heat outside during the summertime, when obviously you don't want to heat your living quarters.

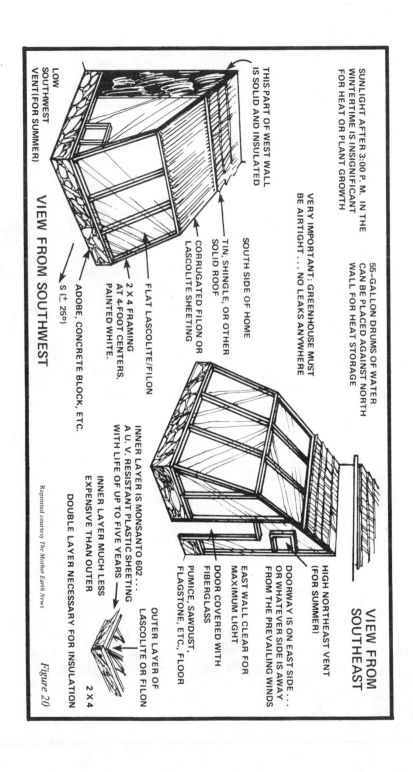

SUNLIGHT AFTER 3:00 P.M. IN THE WINTERTIME IS INSIGNIFICANT FOR HEAT OR PLANT GROWTH

55-GALLON DRUMS OF WATER CAN BE PLACED AGAINST NORTH WALL FOR HEAT STORAGE

VERY IMPORTANT: GREENHOUSE MUST BE AIRTIGHT . . . . NO LEAKS ANYWHERE

THIS PART OF WEST WALL IS SOLID AND INSULATED

LOW SOUTHWEST VENT(FOR SUMMER)

VIEW FROM SOUTHWEST

SOUTH SIDE OF HOME

TIN, SHINGLE, OR OTHER SOLID ROOF

CORRUGATED FILON OR LASCOLITE SHEETING

FLAT LASCOLITE/FILON

2 X 4 FRAMING AT 4-FOOT CENTERS, PAINTED WHITE.

ADOBE, CONCRETE BLOCK, ETC.

S (± 25°)

VIEW FROM SOUTHEAST

HIGH NORTHEAST VENT (FOR SUMMER)

DOORWAY IS ON EAST SIDE . . . . OR WHATEVER SIDE IS AWAY FROM THE PREVAILING WINDS

EAST WALL CLEAR FOR MAXIMUM LIGHT

DOOR COVERED WITH FIBERGLASS

PUMICE, SAWDUST, FLAGSTONE, ETC., FLOOR

INNER LAYER IS MONSANTO 602 . . . A U. V. RESISTANT PLASTIC SHEETING WITH LIFE OF UP TO FIVE YEARS

INNER LAYER MUCH LESS EXPENSIVE THAN OUTER

OUTER LAYER OF LASCOLITE OR FILON

DOUBLE LAYER NECESSARY FOR INSULATION

2 X 4

Reprinted courtesy *The Mother Earth News*

Figure 20

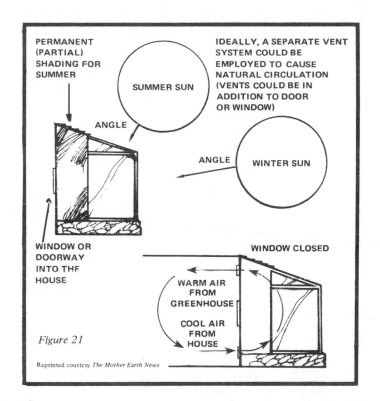

PERMANENT (PARTIAL) SHADING FOR SUMMER

SUMMER SUN

ANGLE

IDEALLY, A SEPARATE VENT SYSTEM COULD BE EMPLOYED TO CAUSE NATURAL CIRCULATION (VENTS COULD BE IN ADDITION TO DOOR OR WINDOW)

ANGLE

WINTER SUN

WINDOW OR DOORWAY INTO THE HOUSE

WINDOW CLOSED

WARM AIR FROM GREENHOUSE

COOL AIR FROM HOUSE

Figure 21

Reprinted courtesy *The Mother Earth News*

Photo 19

INDEX